# Men's Fitness magazine
## COMPLETE GUIDE TO
# Running Cycling and Swimming

By **Jon Lipsey**

Design **Ian Jackson**
Photography **Tom Miles**
Sub Editor **Matthew Hurrell**
Contributors **Lucy Miller, Pete Muir,
Sam Murphy, Chris Sidwells, Joe Warner**
Thanks to **Dan Bullock and Bram Montgomery
at SwimForTri (swimfortri.com) and
Fitness First (fitnessfirst.co.uk)**

For more information on *Men's Fitness* magazine, go to mensfitnessmagazine.co.uk.
To subscribe call 0844 8440081.
For international licensing enquiries contact Winne Liesenfeld on (+44) 020 7907 6134.

Dennis Publishing

# Contents

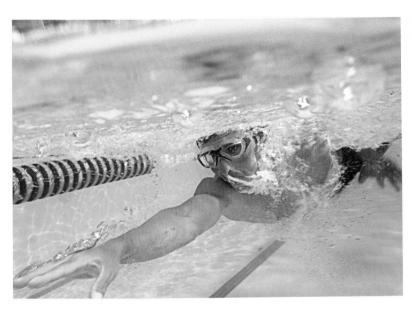

# And you're off

**W**elcome to *Running, Cycling and Swimming*, brought to you by the people at *Men's Fitness* magazine. This is the ultimate guide for anyone who wants to improve their cardiovascular fitness by doing the sports of running, road cycling, swimming and triathlon. The benefits of cardiovascular – also known as cardio – exercise are explained overleaf. If you follow the advice in this book you'll improve your stamina and be able to exercise at a higher intensity. You'll also enjoy a range of health benefits, such as reduced heart-attack risk, as well as boosting your overall wellbeing thanks to your body's increased production of feel-good hormones. Start now, and you'll look and feel better in no time.

### What's in *Running, Cycling and Swimming*?

The book is split up into five main sections. We start with a chapter on running, which guides you through buying the right kit, how to vary your runs and how to stay injury free. There are also step-by-step running workouts and training plans for popular race distances. In the bike chapter, we go through the main types of road bike, as well as giving essential technique and training advice. The goal-specific training plans will help you put what you've learned into practice. The swimming chapter includes a comprehensive guide to technique, drills and types of swim. The detailed training plans are designed to boost both your skill and fitness levels. In the nutrition chapter, you'll get advice on how to eat for more energy, a week-long meal plan and tips on pre- and post-race fuel. The final section explores the sport of triathlon, which brings together the three sports featured earlier in the book. You'll find advice on buying the right gear, how to train and how to succeed on race day.

# What is cardio?

You're familiar with the term, but what exactly is cardio fitness and why should you try to improve it?

Put simply, cardio fitness refers to your body's ability to generate energy through the circulation of blood and oxygen. You can improve your cardio fitness by doing aerobic exercise, which is any activity that you can sustain for more than a few minutes that requires your heart and lungs to work harder in order to meet your body's increased demand for oxygen. Running, cycling, swimming and triathlon will all increase your aerobic fitness, helping you to exercise for longer and burn more calories, as well as improving your heart and lung function. A complete training regime, including sport-specific gym work, will also strengthen your muscles, joints and ligaments, reducing your chances of getting injured.

## Benefits of cardio
Aerobic exercise will make your heart stronger, which means it can pump more blood with each beat. Because it can pump more blood in a single beat, it doesn't have to beat as frequently, which is why cardio exercise can help to lower your resting heart rate.

Your muscles will also become more adept at consuming oxygen. This is because of an increase in the number of enzymes that transport oxygen to your muscles. Once oxygen has reached your muscles, you'll be able to burn fat and carbohydrate more efficiently thanks to heightened activity in mitochondria, the little powerhouses in muscle cells that get you moving.

Aerobic exercise has also been shown to have a host of other health benefits, such as reduced cancer and heart-attack risk as well as a positive effect on your mood.

## How to train
Just getting out there and exercising will help, but you need to have a structure to your training if you want to get the best results. The key is to exercise with your heart rate high enough to create a training effect, but without going too hard and fatiguing your muscles too early in the session. A good way of judging how hard to train is to go fast enough so that you don't find it easy to have a conversation, but can still talk a bit. You also have to do different types of training session

if you want to make sure you keep stimulating your body.

## Weighty issue
One of the most surprising things about developing aerobic fitness is that it requires you to train muscle strength. When you're running, for example, each footstrike sends several times your bodyweight through your body, so your muscles have to be strong enough to cope with that force. The exercises in the Run, Bike, Swim and Triathlon chapters of this book will strengthen your muscles in a sport-specific way to handle impacts, improve your power output and help guard against injury.

## Avoiding injury
Building the amount of exercise you do gradually and ensuring you have good technique will help minimise your injury risk. Some of the sports in this book, such as cycling, involve hours of repetitive training, but you can reduce your injury risk by working out to give yourself strong, stable joints. Exercise itself doesn't weaken your joints, but the wrong type of exercise at the wrong time can cause problems.

## Golden rules of cardio

**■ Make training progressive**
You should do something different in each session by adding either time, intensity or a new challenge.

**■ Take recovery seriously**
If you don't give your body enough time and the right nutrition to recover, you won't get fitter.

**■ Cross-train**
Do more than one activity if you want

functional, all-round fitness that you can transfer across sports.

**■ Build muscle for speed**
You can't go faster without getting stronger, so make sure you factor gym work into your training regime.

**■ Get racing**
Sign up for a competitive event to give yourself extra motivation and your training a time-specific focus.

## Lung capacity test

To gauge your lung capacity, take a party balloon and stretch it. Now blow into it as hard as you can to empty your lungs. Pinch the end and measure the diameter. Do this three times and calculate the average figure. Do this test every two weeks to see how you're improving.

# part 1

# Run

Get faster and run longer with this complete
gear, technique and training guide

# Up and running

## Get on the fast track to fitness with this complete running guide

The great thing about running is that you already know how to do it. Even if you have never done any recreational running, you can still lace up a pair of trainers and head outside for a jog. You may have to start with short distances at an easy pace but, whatever your level of fitness, if you stick with it you will gradually get faster and be able to run for longer. Making progress in the safest and quickest way possible, however, is a bit more complicated. This section guides you through everything you need to get the maximum return from your efforts.

### How to use this section

Before you start running, you need to make sure you have the right kit. The most important thing is to buy a pair of trainers that suits your running style. The gear pages in this section tell you how to buy a suitable pair, as well as giving you the essential information on running clothing and accessories.

There is also more than one way of running. To maximise your fitness benefits and minimise your injury risk you should incorporate a variety of runs, outlined in Training Methods (p26-29), into your programme. These runs should vary in length and intensity so that they challenge your body in different ways.

Another way to improve is to do some running-specific gym work to complement the time you spend pounding pavements. Having strong muscles, joints and tendons will make you a more efficient runner and massively reduce your risk of a running-related injury. Follow the strength and stability programmes in this section and you'll notice improvements to both your speed and your endurance. Of course, no runner is immune to injury and some of the problems you may encounter, such as runner's knee, shin splints and lower-back pain, are all explored later in the chapter.

Once you're kitted out and familiar with the key training techniques, it's time to start following a plan. The five programmes starting on p44 give you a day-by-day breakdown of what you should be doing, from a walk to run plan, to the full marathon, with 5K, 10K and half-marathon plans in between. We've also picked out the UK's top races, as well as the best events from around the world, so you have something to work towards.

## Benefits of running

### ■ It slows the ageing process

Our bones and muscles are designed to accommodate the stresses placed upon them. If you sit at a desk all day and generally lead a sedentary lifestyle, your bones, muscles and joints will only be as strong as they need to be to cope with that level of activity. If, however, you do exercise such as running, they will strengthen to respond to that stress, making you feel fitter even though you're getting older.

### ■ It improves your circulatory system

Running will lower your blood pressure and help to maintain the elasticity of your arteries, which reduces your risk of suffering from a heart attack or stroke. When you run, your arteries expand to about three times the size they are when you're sedentary, which helps promote blood flow.

### ■ It improves your respiratory system

Running requires you to pump more blood around your body than when you're resting. That's because you need to get more oxygen to your muscles in order to make them work hard enough to move you forwards. Happily, regular running will increase the number of capillaries, the tiny blood vessels that supply blood to your lungs, which makes your respiratory system more efficient.

# Personal trainers

## Using the right gear can help you to run better. Here's what you need

If you want to get the most out of your running, you need the right gear. That doesn't mean you have to buy the most expensive pair of trainers in the shop. You should, however, go to a specialist running store. They can help you find a shoe that will suit how you run and help minimise your injury risk. Wearing kit made from wicking fabric, which removes sweat from the skin, will make your runs more comfortable and enjoyable. Using running gadgets such as a heart rate monitor or MP3 player can keep you motivated and entertained during tough sessions.

## Five steps to buying the perfect trainers

Here's what a good running shop assistant should ask you before you choose your shoes

### 1 Where will you be running?
The grip, support and cushioning you need depends on the surface you'll be pounding. Road runners need more cushioning but less grip than those sticking to off-road routes.

### 2 Do you have any injuries?
If you have a history of running-related injuries (such as runner's knee or shin splints), this should influence the pair you wear. Someone who has dodgy knees or who has suffered from shin splints may need extra support around the arch of the foot, for example.

### 3 Can I watch you run?
The shop assistant needs to identify your running style. They should either ask you to run on a treadmill in the shop or watch you run outside in the street. They need to see, for example, whether you pronate (collapsing in at the ankles) when you run. If you do pronate, you may need a pair of motion-control shoes.

### 4 How long and how far will you be running?
Your feet swell when they're hot. The longer and further you run, the steamier they'll get. Ideally you want a pair with half a thumb-width of space at the toe.

### 5 How do they feel?
If you're not entirely happy with the shoes, you don't have to buy them. Rather than pressuring you into making a purchase, a good assistant will listen to your feedback and offer you a selection of shoes so you can pick the one that suits you best.

## Main types of shoe

The type of shoe you wear will depend on your running style and where you run. These are the main categories

### Stability shoes
These all-rounders offer a good level of cushioning, as well as extra support on the inside of the midsole (the foam layer between the part of the sole that comes into contact with the ground and the part that encases your foot) to prevent inward turning of the ankles.
**Pictured: Brooks Adrenaline GTS8, £80**

### Motion-control shoes
Aimed at overpronators (people who collapse in excessively at the ankles), these are the most rigid road running trainers. They usually include a medial post (a firm section under the arch of your foot) and are heavy but durable.
**Pictured: Saucony Stabil MC5, £70**

### Cushioned shoes
With the least added stability and the softest midsoles, cushioned shoes should be worn by neutral runners who don't pronate. They're particularly good for efficient runners or those who have comparatively rigid feet.
**Pictured: Nike Air Zoom Vomero+ 2, £90**

### Trail shoes
Built for off-road running, they have more rugged upper and outer sections than road-running shoes. You get more protection, which you'll need if you're running on mixed, obstacle-strewn terrain. They're less responsive, but the ground you run on will be softer than concrete or tarmac, so you need less cushioning.
**Pictured: Salomon XT Wing, £80**

Wear the right gear for a smoother, faster run

### T-shirt
Made with wicking material, which moves sweat away from your skin to the outer layer of the fabric, where it evaporates. It should be cut to work with the way your body moves.
**Cold weather option:** lightweight waterproof running jacket.
**Pictured: New Balance Tech T, £16**

### Shorts
These should also be lightweight, made with wicking fabric and have an inner layer to help protect against chafing. Shorter shorts have traditionally been associated with faster running but longer modern running shorts won't inhibit speed.
**Cold weather option:** technical running tights.
**Pictured: Adidas Supernova baggy short, £27**

### Socks
Running socks have extra padding at high-impact contact areas such as the toes, ball of the foot and heel to help avoid blistering. Some have two layers, so friction is concentrated on the fabric rather than your skin.
**Cold weather option:** woollen running socks.
**Pictured: Nike Dri-Fit 3.0 cushioned quarter running sock, £5**

# Know your trainers

## How to identify and understand the key components of your shoes

**Last**

This is a mould that determines the inside shape of the shoe. It's based on average foot shapes but varies from one manufacturer to the other. That's partly why similar shoes from different brands feel different.

**Upper**

Every part of the shoe above the sole. Look for breathable mesh fabric to help regulate the temperature of your feet.

**Toe Box**

As the name suggests, this is the part of the shoe that holds your toes. A constricting toe box can cause bruising and give you black toenails.

**Midsole**

The most technical part of the shoe controls foot movement and absorbs shock. Stability and motion control shoes have extra support on the inside of the midsole.

**■ Insole**
These line the inside of the shoe and are worn to provide extra comfort and cushioning.

**■ Heel counter**
This is a stiffened piece of plastic inside the back of the shoe, which is designed to hold your heel in place and reduce sideways movement.

**■ Medial post**
A wedge of higher than normal density foam in the midsole that provides pronation control to promote efficient movement through the gait cycle.

**■ Outsole**
The rubber section of the shoe that's in contact with the ground. It provides grip and helps to determine the flexibility of the shoe.

## Running-friendly gadgets

Use technology to give your training a boost

**■ Heart-rate monitor**
These devices, which include a chest strap and wrist monitor, give you real-time feedback on how hard you're working. You can use that information to create training sessions and track your progress. They're also useful for heart-rate target interval sessions.
**Pictured: Polar RS800, £384.50**

**■ GPS monitor**
Uses GPS technology to work out where you are so you can tell how far and fast you have run. They can also offer features that trace the relief of your runs, store your data to assess progress and allow you to race against your previous runs.
**Pictured: Garmin Forerunner 405, from £229**

**■ MP3 player**
Studies have shown that listening to music while you exercise can improve your performance. Go for a lightweight, option that you can control without having to slow down.
**Pictured: Apple iPod shuffle, from £32**

# Best foot forward

## Maximise your running efficiency by concentrating on your technique

**W**hen it comes to running technique, coaches and sports scientists generally agree on one thing, that there's no such thing as correct running technique. That's why British distance runner Paula Radcliffe has managed to win marathons with a strange nodding head style. Try to copy her and you're more likely to end up with a brace rather than a medal around our neck. That's because you should do what comes naturally to you.

This anything goes concept makes running a beginner-friendly sport. You may not have the stamina to go out on long runs when you start but there's no technical reason why you shouldn't get out there. There are, however, general pointers that you can follow that will make you run more efficiently. Being aware of your own running style will also allow you to explore subtle adjustments to your technique that can help you to run further and faster.

### Footstrike
The part of your foot that hits the ground first determines your style of footstrike. Toe strikers make contact with the ground with the ball of their foot and their toes first whereas heel strikers land on their heels. Toe strikers land on the ball of their foot and roll back to the heel as they push off the ground. The majority of people, however, are heel strikers, who land heel first, rolling forwards through the foot and pushing off the ground with their toes. Most running coaches advise against trying to change your natural footstrike but there are running

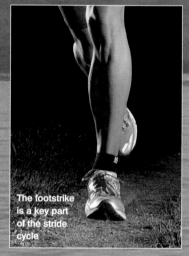

The footstrike is a key part of the stride cycle

methods, such as the Pose technique (described on page 23), which suggest that using a particular footstrike can make you run faster. Beginners should not try to alter their footstrike but more advanced runners may want to explore adjustments with the advice of a coach.

### Stride cycle
Your foot should land slightly in front of your centre of gravity so that when your foot is in full contact with the ground it is directly under your centre of gravity. You should have a slight bend in the knee to soften the impact. Good core stability will allow you to stay tall throughout the stride rather than collapsing slightly on impact. Once your foot is in full contact with the ground you roll forward towards your toes to begin the drive phase. Your standing leg will straighten, pushing you forwards

with power from your hamstrings and glutes. Finally, your calf will add extra forward propulsion as your foot leaves the ground. Once your foot has left the ground it will extend backwards, rising up slightly before coming forwards lead by the knee. As your speed increases, knee lift should become higher and more purposeful to generate power.

### Pace
Two key aspects of determining pace are stride length and turnover (the number of strides you take over a set distance). Beginners who want to increase their pace are better off concentrating on increasing turnover rather than stride length because it involves less disruption to your natural style. Once you're more advanced, you can practice lengthening your stride.

### Arm position
Your arms help develop a smooth running rhythm. Generally, the quicker you run, the more your arms pump to move you forward. Keep your arms close to your sides and avoid taking your elbows and hands back too far because that will encourage trunk rotation, which can slow you down.

### Relaxation
One thing that every runner should do is aim to be as relaxed as possible. Tensing your muscles wastes energy, leaving you less in the tank for propelling yourself forward. The quicker you run, the harder it is to stay relaxed but it's worth remembering that even 100-metre sprinters try to avoid tensing up while they run.

## Hill running

### Adjust your stride to go faster up and down hills

When you run up a hill, shorten your stride and reduce your pace so that your rate of perceived exertion (how hard you're working) doesn't change from flat to incline. Because of the slope, you're more likely to make contact with the ground with your forefoot first rather than your heel. You may also need to push down harder to gain the vertical movement required to take you up the hill. Running downhill may feel easy but can put a lot of stress on your knees and quads. To minimise the impact, stay relaxed and don't lean back.

## Alternative styles

### ■ Chi Running

This method involves an adjustment to both your attitude and your technique. It was devised by US running coach and Tai Chi expert, Danny Dreyer and the aim is to stay relaxed while you run so that you can reduce your rate of perceived exertion. You do that by focusing on your movement rather than the discomfort of working at a high intensity.

The key change to your technique is to lean forward at the heels, as opposed to the waist or hips, which would place extra strain on your quads and lower back. To make sure you maintain balance, extend your legs when you pick up your heels.

The idea of leaning forwards slightly to use momentum to assist your movement isn't particularly controversial. The Chi running idea that you should strike the ground first with your midfoot is, however, more divisive. Most running coaches would advise against trying to alter your footstrike without expert assistance so, if you are going to give Chi running a try, you're best off doing it under the supervision of a running coach.

# Great strides

These running form pointers can help you run smoother and expend less energy

■ Relax your jaw and neck. Tensing up is a sign that you're tiring.

■ Relaxing your hands will help reduce tension in your arms and shoulders and will avoid wasting energy. If you need to clench your fists because you're cold, wear running gloves.

■ Avoid swinging your arms back and forth in front of your chest because it can restrict breathing.

■ Your hips should be in line with your shoulders and you should try to avoid lateral movement because this will slow you down.

■ If you're distance running, you want a lower knee lift because it will use less energy.

■ If you want to increase your speed, reducing how much you bounce will cut the time your feet are in contact with the ground. This will make you faster but can be more tiring.

■ Visualise growing taller as you run, because slouching can compromise your posture and core stability.

■ Keep your shoulders relaxed. If they're stiff you tend to rotate them more, which causes an opposing movement in the hips and wastes energy.

■ Your arms should swing naturally like pendulums. Don't try to generate power from the arms if you're running at jogging pace.

■ Breath from the diaphragm (the pit of the stomach), not the chest. When you breath from your chest, you pull your shoulders up, which is inefficient.

■ Let your knees, rather than your feet, lead your legs. Landing with your feet in front of your knees will act as a break so plant your foot under your knee.

■ About 80 per cent of runners are heel strikers, which means they land on their heel, roll through the foot and push off with the toes. If you run like this, hold your torso upright, keeping your spine straight.

## Alternative styles

### ■ Pose method

This technique was invented in the 1970s by Russian sports scientist Dr Nicholas Romanov. The central idea is that you should use gravity to take you forwards because that reduces the effort you expend in propelling yourself forwards. You do that by leaning forward when you run, landing on your forefoot with your knee slightly bent. Your strides should be short and your turnover rapid. Do all that and, according to Romanov, you'll run faster, use less energy and reduce your risk of suffering from knee pain. High profile devotees include top British triathletes Tim Don and Andrew Johns.

The argument against adopting the Pose method is that your muscles, joints and ligaments develop naturally over years to suit your running style. Tamper with that style and you could increase your injury risk. You may also be poor at executing the Pose technique, rocking back from forefoot to heel before moving forwards again, which will slow you down. As with Chi running, the answer is to explore the method with guidance from an expert.

Pose method runners strike the ground toes first

# Pre-run routine

## Before your main run, do this warm-up to prepare your body

Warming up properly at the beginning of your run is essential to reduce your risk of injury. A warm-up will raise your core temperature and prepare your joints and muscles for the exertion to come. By doing a gentle run and some dynamic stretches, your heart will beat faster, pumping oxygen and nutrients to your muscles and raising your body's temperature.

Warm muscles are more elastic, meaning you can run freely with less chance of injury. A warm-up is less important on recovery runs, but vital before an interval session, where you're asking your body to work at high intensity. Start your session by jogging at an easy pace for five to ten minutes, then do the dynamic stretches on the opposite page.

# Dynamic stretches

Once you have completed your warm-up run, do the following stretches to target the main running muscles. Dynamic stretches involve moving continuously, placing the muscles under increasing pressure with each repetition, which prepares the muscles and joints for the main run. Recent research suggests that you should avoid doing static stretches, where you hold the stretch to let the muscle relax, before a run because they can slow the rate of muscle activation rather than loosening you up.

### Walking lunge

Do this to stretch your glutes, hamstrings and hip flexors. Step into a lunge so that your front knee is bent at 90˚. Bring your trailing leg through to stand upright and step into a lunge with your other leg. Repeat the move on alternate legs for 30 seconds.

### Squats

This stretch warms up your glutes, hamstrings, quads and calves. Start with your arms out in front of you and sink down into a squat. Rise back up and pause briefly before repeating the move for 30 seconds.

### Leg swings

Do this to activate your hip flexors and glutes. Stand on one leg and swing your other leg out in front of you. Without bending your knee, swing your leg back behind you, taking care not to rotate at the hips. Repeat for 20 seconds then switch legs.

### High knees

This stretch flexes the hips and shoulders, as well as mobilising the glutes and quads. Take a step forward, exaggerating the knee lift and arm swing. Repeat the move on alternate legs for 30 seconds.

# Varying your runs

Train smarter to increase your running speed and endurance

Running the same route at the same pace soon gets boring and will limit the rate and extent of your progress. Steady-paced runs do have their place. They boost your endurance, making your muscles more fatigue-resistant, improving fat utilisation and increasing the amount of oxygen transported to your muscles. But they can't do everything and that's where other sessions come in. Faster runs can help increase your aerobic capacity, improve your running economy (your pace at any given heart rate) and perfect your technique.

Try to follow a training plan that includes different types of run. Swedish researchers found that the best way to increase heart volume is through steady distance running, while the best way to increase cardiac output

(the amount of blood pumped out by the heart per minute) is to run at high intensity. Combining the two gives you both benefits. Here are the main types of running session.

## Tempo running

Also known as threshold running, because it relates to the 'lactate threshold' – the point at which lactic acid, a by-product of intense exercise, builds up in the muscles faster than it can be removed – is one of the most effective ways of improving your ability to cover distance at speed. A study found that adding tempo running to a distance running programme for six weeks resulted in an average two-minute reduction in 10K race times. The aim is to run at an intensity that is on, or slightly below, your lactate

threshold. Lactic acid build up makes your muscles feel like either jelly or concrete. But if you can manage to hover around the threshold, rather than cross it, you'll nudge it upwards, as well as teach yourself to build up a tolerance to lactic acid and improve your body's overall efficiency. According to the journal *Peak Performance*, the lactate threshold usually occurs at an intensity of between 85 and 92 per cent of maximum heart rate. There are two ways of tackling tempo running: continuous efforts (such as a 20-minute run) or long intervals with relatively short recoveries (6x5 minutes with 90 seconds recovery). Don't take longer recoveries because the objective is to boost economy not pure speed. You don't want to be fully recovered between each repetition.

# Interval training

Want to know the best way to run faster? Train faster. Sounds obvious, but the trouble is running at your maximum pace isn't likely to be sustainable for long. That's where interval training comes in. By separating bursts of high-intensity running with bouts of rest or jogging, you can do high-quality training without killing yourself. Research in the *Journal Of Sports Medicine And Physical Fitness* found that recreational runners gained a six per cent improvement in VO2 max (the body's capacity to use oxygen) after six weeks of interval training. Fast-paced running also improves your leg turnover (the number of strides you take per minute), gets you used to

working at a higher level of intensity and recruits more muscle fibres. Interval training can be manipulated to meet your goals: short intervals with long recoveries (such as 400m with a 90-120 second recovery) work on pure speed, while at the other end of the spectrum, longer intervals with shorter recoveries boost endurance and lactate tolerance.

The variables you have to play with are effort level, the length or distance of the effort, the length of the recovery and the number of intervals you perform within a session. Whatever your objective, try to achieve the same pace on all your intervals within a session – the last one should be the same pace as the first.

## Interval time

Do these interval sessions to improve your running speed

### ■ Pyramid interval

This session builds your bursts of speed up gradually and tapers off at the end as your energy levels are dwindling. Use a running watch to time your intervals. If you can't complete the session, do as much as you can and do more as you improve.

10 minutes easy jog
30 seconds fast, 60 seconds recovery
30 seconds fast, 60 seconds recovery
60 seconds fast, 60 seconds recovery
60 seconds fast, 60 seconds recovery
90 seconds fast, 60 seconds recovery
90 seconds fast, 60 seconds recovery
60 seconds fast, 60 seconds recovery
60 seconds fast, 60 seconds recovery
30 seconds fast, 60 seconds recovery
30 seconds fast, 60 seconds recovery
10 minutes easy jog

### ■ Paired intervals

This session keeps the speed bursts constant, but alternates between short and long rests to get your body used to working at high intensity without being too taxing. Do this on a running track or using a GPS monitor so you know how far you have run. If you can't complete the session, do as much as you can and do more as you improve.

10 minutes easy jog
300 metres fast, 100 metres recovery
300 metres fast, 300 metres recovery
300 metres fast, 100 metres recovery
300 metres fast, 300 metres recovery
300 metres fast, 100 metres recovery
300 metres fast, 300 metres recovery
300 metres fast, 100 metres recovery
300 metres fast, 300 metres recovery
10 minutes easy jog

## Fartlek

The term means 'speed play' in Swedish and, as far as running is concerned, this means mixing steady running with bursts of effort, usually dictated by the route you're running. For example, using a change in terrain or incline to instigate a change in speed, or using landmarks, such as trees or dustbins, as your markers. Fartlek challenges both your aerobic and anaerobic energy systems because you'll be varying your pace from one at which you can easily get enough oxygen to your muscles to one where you cannot, causing you to go into 'oxygen debt'. It's a great way to train for multi-sprint sports, such as football or rugby, because it mimics the stop-start nature of these sports. It's also a simple way of introducing speed work to your regime because it doesn't bog you down with number crunching.

## Hill repetitions

Hill training will pay dividends even if you don't have your sights set on a mountain marathon. The effort to overcome gravity recruits more muscle fibres than running on flat ground, as well as working the cardiovascular system harder.

Unless you are training for a specific event with steep inclines, select a hill that isn't steep enough to compromise your technique. Shorten and quicken your stride a little, and use the propulsion of your arms to assist you as you climb.

Hill repetitions are usually performed 'hard up, easy down', but for variety, you could try a Kenyan hill session where you also run hard down the hill. The downhill element increases your cadence and stride length, getting your nerves and muscles accustomed to faster running, and strengthens your leg muscles and connective tissues. But there's a price: according to research by the University of Colorado, a hill with a 9 per cent descent increases impact forces by 54 per cent. So don't be surprised if your thighs feel like raw meat the next day.

## Off-road running

Running off-road offers a mental break from the monotony of road running. Research by the University of Essex shows that exercising in a natural environment boosts mood more than running in urban settings. But it also presents a new challenge for your leg muscles. The less stable surface and undulating terrain work the lower body more than flat road running, according to research from the University of Western Australia. It also improves balance and stability, and the softer landing reduces the risk of picking up impact-related injuries.

If you can maintain the same pace off road as you can on road, your energy expenditure will be greater. But in reality most of us slow our pace down on tougher terrain. Performing fartlek or intervals is a good way of injecting some speed into your off road runs.

# Recovery starts here

Follow this post-run routine to help your body recover quickly

Cooling down after a run will lower your heart rate and help flush lactic acid out of your muscles so you can recover quickly. Spend the last five to ten minutes of your session bringing your heart rate back down by running at an easy pace then do the stretches outlined below.

## Post-run stretches

Static stretches relax your muscles, which are then held under tension for a period of time without moving. This helps lengthen your muscles, which is particularly helpful for keeping flexible and achieving a good range of motion. Get into the stretch position and allow your muscles to relax. As you place pressure on the muscle you should be able to feel it relaxing and lengthening. You can slowly increase the pressure on the muscle throughout the duration of the stretch, but never force it or 'bounce' because that can damage the muscle. If you feel pain, stop immediately.

## Quad stretch

Stand on one leg and pull your heel back towards your buttock, keeping your back straight. If you struggle to keep your balance, hold on to a tree or a wall. Hold the stretch for 20 seconds, then switch legs. Repeat on both sides.

### Hamstring stretch

Stand with your front leg straight and your back leg slightly bent. With your front foot toes pointing up, push your hips back to feel the stretch in your hamstrings. Hold the position for 20 seconds, then switch legs. Repeat on both sides.

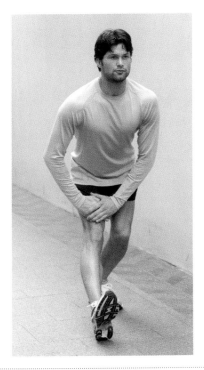

### Calf stretch

Stand with your feet a stride's length apart. Bend your front knee slightly and keep your back leg straight with the heel pushing down into the ground until you feel the stretch in your calf. Hold that position for 20 seconds, then switch legs. Repeat on both sides.

### Hip stretch

Step forwards into a lunge. Once you are in the down position, push your hips forward. Keep your back straight and your hips aligned. Hold that position for 20 seconds, then switch legs. Repeat on both sides.

### Glute stretch

Stand on one leg and balance the bottom of your raised shin on your standing knee. Hold on to a wall or a tree to stabilise yourself and sink down until you feel the stretch in your glutes. Hold that position for 20 seconds, then switch legs. Repeat on both sides.

# Running power

## Inject speed into your stride with this running power routine

Time spent pounding the streets gives you a good base of running fitness. But if you want to keep chipping away at your personal bests, you'll need to complement your runs with some structured gym work. The key here is to build muscle endurance rather than muscle mass, so you should perform relatively high repetitions of the exercise for each set. Do that and you'll have the strength for a sprint at the end of a race, picking up places near the finish line as weaker runners start to fade.

You'll also get overall speed benefits. In one recent American study, subjects who did a ten-week resistance training programme improved their 10K running time by 80 seconds. That's because having stronger cells means you need to recruit fewer muscle fibres for each stride, which, in turn, means you need less oxygen to run at the same pace. Do the following exercises in order once or twice a week on non-running days to give yourself a new lease of pace.

### 1 Bulgarian split squat

**Sets: 3 Reps: 15 each side**

■ Select a weight that's comfortable but testing.
■ Place your back leg up on a bench behind to focus the effort on your other leg.
■ Lower yourself down as far as possible.
■ Drive back up, keeping your core braced.

**Why do it?** This is a great strength-building move for your quads and hams, and working each leg individually will balance out your body.

### Dumb-bell 'run'
**Sets:** 3 **Reps:** 12 each side

■ Keep your forward leg braced.
■ Pump your arms as if you were running.
■ Keep your shoulders back and level.
■ Alternate legs with each set.

**Why do it?** A strong upper body is vital for maintaining form and power when running. This exercise is as specific to the running action as possible.

### Overhead squat
**Sets:** 3 **Reps:** 15

■ Select a weight that's comfortable but testing.
■ Place your hands two shoulder widths apart on the bar.
■ Keep the bar directly above your shoulders.
■ Lower as far as possible until your thighs are level with the floor.

**Why do it?** Holding the bar above your head activates the core muscles and forces your body to stabilise the weight and stay in alignment as you lower and drive using your thighs and glutes.

### 4 Stiff-legged Romanian deadlift
**Sets:** 3 **Reps:** 15

■ Stand with your feet hip-width apart with an overhand grip on a barbell.
■ Bend over at the hips, keeping your back flat and your legs almost straight as you lower the weight.

**Why do it?** This classic strength-building move really works the hamstrings on the back of the thigh, a vital running muscle. It also uses the lower back in a stabilising role and the upper back in a power role.

## 5 Jumping calf raise
**Sets:** 3 **Reps:** 15 each side

■ Place the ball of your foot on a step.
■ Push off your toes to jump in the air.

**Why do it?** Explosive moves such as this target your fast twitch muscle fibres and help reduce the time your foot spends on the ground during each stride.

## 6 Backwards sledgehammer
**Sets:** 3 **Reps:** 12

■ Squat down holding a medicine ball in both hands.
■ Drive up explosively through your heels and onto your toes.
■ Keep your core braced as you throw the ball up and behind.
■ Turn around for the throw back from your partner and go again.

**Why do it?** This explosive move gets your body working against gravity in a single move, giving you strength for maximum efforts on your run.

# Running stability

## Do this efficiency-improving stability workout to stay injury free

For a non-contact sport, running is responsible for a large number of injuries. One of the main reasons for experiencing pain is weakness in key running muscles. Weak quads, for example, can cause soreness around the kneecap. Doing exercises that strengthen your muscles and connective tissue will reduce your chances of suffering a running-related injury, which is essential if you want to enjoy the benefits of an uninterrupted training plan.

It can also improve your running economy (efficiency) because instability in your legs, glutes, hips and core will make your movements excessive and inefficient, causing you to use more oxygen. When your muscles and joints become more stable, there is less unnecessary movement, which in turn reduces your oxygen demand and allows you to up the pace. Do the following workout once or twice a week on non-running days to spend more time on your feet and less time with the physio.

### 1 Medicine ball V-sit
**Sets: 3 Reps:** 10

■ Lie on an exercise mat with your arms held out straight behind your head, holding a medicine ball in both hands.
■ Lift your arms and legs off the floor, keeping them straight and your arms in line with your torso so that your body forms a V-shape.
■ Lift for two seconds, hold for one and lower the medicine ball and your legs down for four seconds.

**Why do it?** To be a strong runner you need a strong core to stabilise and support the movement. By lowering your limbs slowly you cut momentum out of the exercise and make sure that you have no weak spots in the range of motion. The exercise also works your hip flexors, which are important running muscles.

### Side-on hurdle

**Sets:** 3 **Reps:** 12 each leg

■ Lift your knees as high as possible and keep your shoulders back.
■ Place both feet on the floor before hurdling again.

**Why do it?** When you start to tire your knees drop and you lose speed, so this drill aims to improve your biomechanics as well as your hip flexor and quad strength endurance.

### Calf kick

**Sets:** 3 **Time:** 30 seconds

■ Run along with very short steps.
■ Don't allow your heels to touch the floor.
■ Kick your legs out ahead of you so that your knees are extended.
■ Use your calves to catch you and push you forwards.

**Why do it?** When you run faster you use the middle and ball of your foot. This prepares your calves to pick up the load and turn your feet over quickly.

### Gym ball hamstring curl

**Sets:** 3 **Reps:** 10 each side

■ Place one heel on the ball then lift your hips up.
■ Roll the ball in towards your buttocks.
■ Keeping your hips up, roll the ball out and extend your leg.
■ Keep your neck relaxed throughout.

**Why do it?** Lifting your hips up off the floor activates your core. Using one leg to roll the ball in improves the condition of your knee and hip stabilisers while working your hamstrings.

# 5 Stretch band hold

**Sets:** 2 **Reps:** 45 seconds each side

■ Attach a stretch band to a secure anchor on your left then loop it around your right knee, just above the joint.
■ Take your left foot off the ground and balance on one foot, bending your knee slightly so that you can see at least two of your toes.
■ Push the toes of your right foot into the ground to stabilise your leg. Hold for 45 seconds, then swap sides and hold again.

**Why do it?** This exercise works the plantar fascia, which runs underneath your foot and your shin muscle. These muscles can tire towards the end of a race, which will encourage overpronation and your running form can collapse. By strengthening them, you will help to hold your form and prevent injury.

# 6 Medicine ball catch, roll and throw

**Sets:** 3 **Reps:** 10

■ Place both feet solidly on the floor.
■ Catch the ball as it passes overhead.
■ Extend your abs fully then throw the ball back.
■ Aim your throw to one side to introduce some rotation.

**Why do it?** This is a plyometric exercise, which works the core with the upper body and legs to make you stable and powerful throughout your run.

# Injury time

## Reduce your injury risk and speed up recovery with this guide to common running ailments

The never-injured runner is a rare beast but injuries tend to creep up slowly, rather than being caused by one sudden, wrong move. They're often the result of multiple factors. Common causes include muscular imbalances, poor flexibility and incorrect running technique. Training errors, such as wearing the wrong shoes, building up your mileage too quickly and failing to warm up or take rest days also up your injury risk.

This section guides you through the most common problems that affect runners but if the measures suggested don't help within a few days, see a doctor or physiotherapist to get some expert advice.

## Runner's knee

### What is it?
Runner's knee, or patellofemoral pain syndrome (PFPS), is characterised by pain and inflammation at the front of the knee. It's impossible to pinpoint the exact area of pain, because the problem lies beneath the kneecap but is often worse going downstairs or after long periods sitting.

### What's the cause?
The main cause of runner's knee is patella maltracking, which is when the kneecap runs slightly adrift of the grooves on the thigh bone (femur) within which it sits, irritating the surrounding structures. The most common causes of maltracking are a muscular imbalance between the inner and outer quads, or weakness in the gluteus medius, a stabilizing muscle in the pelvis.

### How can I treat it?
The first step is to eliminate the inflammation through a combination of rest, ice and anti-inflammatories. Then it's a matter of redressing the balance of the relevant muscles, usually by strengthening the innermost quad and the gluteus medius. Mobilising the patella manually, or taping it in place, can also help to reposition it.

### Minimise your risk
Check your shoes and running gait because overpronators are more prone to PFPS. Perform one-leg squats to strengthen the gluteus medius and quads.

# Iliotibial band friction syndrome (ITBFS)

## What is it?

Pain and inflammation where the Iliotibial (IT) band (a thickened strip of fascia that runs from the hip to the knee) attaches to the outside edge of the knee, often accompanied by an uncomfortable 'catching' of the IT band on the thigh bone.

## What's the cause?

There are myriad causes. Biomechanical factors, such as having 'bow legs' or a leg length difference can be the culprit. Muscular shortcomings, such as weak glutes or a tight lower back, can also be to blame. Running on a camber, or only in one direction, such as on a running track, can also cause ITBFS.

## How can I treat it?

Ice and anti-inflammatories can help alleviate the pain, while massage along the length of the IT band, using your hand, a tennis ball or foam roller, can help take it off tension, reducing its pull on the knee. The IT band is attached to a muscle in the hip called the tensor fascia latae (TFL), and stretching this muscle, in combination with strengthening the glutes, can help rectify the problem.

## Minimise your risk

Avoid excessive track running or cambered surfaces. Strengthen the gluteals to prevent the TFL stepping in and becoming overly tight. Stretch the TFL and ITB regularly.

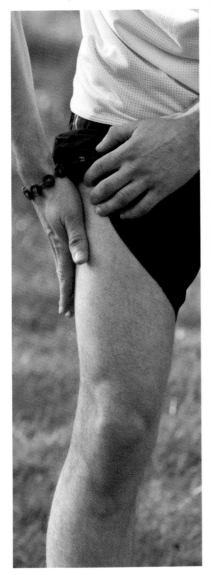

## Rice

Use the rest, ice, compression and elevation (RICE) technique to treat a sudden injury

■ **Rest**

Don't try to run it off. Take your weight off the injured area as soon as you can.

■ **Ice**

Apply ice to the injured area to reduce swelling. Don't apply a hot water bottle because this will increase blood flow to the area.

■ **Compression**

Use a support or bandage to help reduce swelling and keep joints stable.

■ **Elevation**

Try to raise the injured area above the level of your heart. That will help reduce blood flow to the area, which will limit swelling.

## Bring the pain

How doing too much too soon or not getting enough rest can cause problems

■ **Delayed onset muscle soreness**

Delayed onset muscle soreness (DOMS) is muscle pain experienced one to three days after exercise. The exact cause is disputed but recent research suggests it could be triggered by microscopic tears in your muscles and is often brought on by overexertion. Cooling down properly after exercise is thought to reduce the effects.

■ **Overtraining**

While it's the stress, or overload, you put on your body that triggers the physiological changes that enable you to run faster or longer, failing to give yourself sufficient rest means you're not giving your body a chance to make those adaptations. Too much training coupled with insufficient rest can even reduce your fitness and leave you feeling burned out, increasing your injury risk and compromising your immune system.

## Achilles tendonitis

### What is it?
Inflammation of the tendon that joins the two calf muscles to the heel bone – the strongest tendon in the body.

### What's the cause?
Tight calf muscles and stiff ankles can force the Achilles to overwork. Increasing your mileage too quickly or overtraining can also be a factor, as can irritation caused by the heel tab of your shoe rubbing on the tendon.

### How can I treat it?
Reduce your training volume, cutting out speed work and hills, which force you up on your toes more, stressing the tendon. Only run if you can do so pain-free, and ice the area afterwards. Work to improve your calf flexibility by stretching with both a bent and straight leg. A small heel raise in your trainer can also help to unload the tendon.

### Minimise your risk
Don't try to run too far, too quickly and maintain lower leg flexibility by regular stretching and mobility work.

## Shin splints

### What is it?
Shin splints is a 'catch-all' term for shin pain, but it most commonly refers to medial tibial stress syndrome, characterised by pain and inflammation that can feel like bruising, along the medial (inner) border of the shin bone.

### What's the cause?
Running too much for your body's liking, particularly on hard surfaces. Biomechanical factors, such as overpronation and muscular imbalances (excessive tightness or weakness) in the lower leg can also contribute.

### How can I treat it?
Massage and ice or, even better, an ice massage, reduce the inflammation. After that you need to address any underlying tightness or weakness in the muscles of the shin and calf. Warm up the area thoroughly before running and don't run through pain.

### Minimise your risk
Don't increase your mileage too quickly, and vary your surfaces. Maintain strength and flexibility in the lower legs.

## Lower back pain

### What is it?

A non-specific pain or aching in the lower back, either centrally or to one side. It can result in tightness and restricted movement.

### What's the cause?

There are numerous causes of lower back pain in runners, including poor technique and running posture, although the problem is not necessarily a result of running. Previous back pain is the biggest predictor of subsequent problems.

### How can I treat it?

Anti-inflammatories will reduce pain and inflammation but don't use ice. A heat pack is better for releasing tight muscles. Regardless of the cause, improving your posture and addressing imbalances in your core and the surrounding muscles will help. This often entails strengthening the gluteals and deep-lying abdominals and stretching the lower back muscles and hip flexors.

### Minimise your risk

Have your running technique assessed if you have suffered from back pain in the past and work on improving your core stability and spinal mobility.

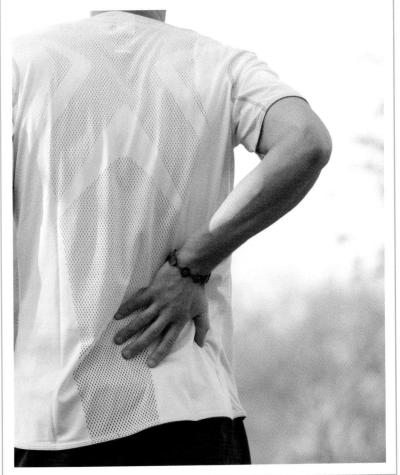

## Preventative measures

Strategies to reduce your chances of getting injured

### ■ Massage

Sports massage will aid your recovery between runs and keep your muscles in good working order. It helps to iron out tension, realigns and stretches muscle fibres and flushes out waste products through improved blood flow. If you see the same practitioner regularly, it can also act as an early warning system against potential problems. If your wallet won't stretch to a fortnightly visit, you can massage your own legs, using long, firm strokes up towards the heart, along the front, back and sides of each leg and save the professional treatment for a couple of days before or after a race.

### ■ Ice baths

Scientific opinion is still divided on whether post-run ice baths have a positive or negative affect on recovery. Advocates, such as marathon runner Paula Radcliffe, believe that plunging your legs into icy water helps to shift lactic acid, which can cause muscle soreness. Others take a different view. A team of researchers from Melbourne University recently claimed that ice baths can increase discomfort. On balance, it's best decided according to personal preference. If you think they work, use one after a run for up to ten minutes at a temperature no lower than ten degrees.

# Instant improvement

## Get ahead of the pack with these quick-hit running tips

**Run in the afternoon**
Going for a run in the afternoon is likely to result in a better workout. Studies have consistently shown that body temperature naturally peaks in the late afternoon, meaning that muscles are warmer and more flexible, strength is at its peak, resting heart rate and blood pressure are low, and exertion is perceived to be easier.

**Run with music**
According to a 2004 study, running while listening to music has been shown to significantly increase speed, energy expenditure and oxygen intake without an increase in perceived effort, compared with running without music. Just make sure you pay extra attention to vehicles, cyclists and any other potential hazards.

**Reward yourself**
If you're struggling to find the motivation to complete your training regime, promise to reward yourself if you stick to your plan. Even better, reward yourself with a new pair of trainers or a running gadget to keep you motivated.

**Get out there**
On days when you don't feel like running, get changed into your running gear, warm up and then make a decision about whether or not you want to exercise. More often than not, you'll head out for your run.

**Take a deep breath**
To make sure that you are running tall and have good posture, you need to minimise the pressure on your diaphragm. You can do that by taking a deep breath to straighten your upper body and maintaining that position after you have exhaled.

**Join a club**
Joining a running club is a great way to step up your running. Being around other keen runners gives you motivation and you'll pick up tips from other members. You don't have to be an experienced runner because most clubs offer a range of speed groups. Regular club races are good for making you run at your maximum effort and are useful for measuring your progress.

**Buy a heart rate monitor**
Determining your heart rate is the best indicator of exertion. A heart rate monitor details your current level of effort, allowing you to ensure that you stick rigidly to a training schedule that includes low, medium and high-intensity workouts.

**Have a goal**
Organised races, even short ones, are the best way of measuring your progress. Once you have signed up – and paid – to enter a race, you will be more likely to be motivated and train than if you have nothing to aim for.

## Consistency is key

You're better off running a shorter route or running at a lower intensity than you had planned than you are skipping a session altogether. This approach will get you into the mindset of never missing runs.

## Do what you can

If you're really struggling for time, then do what you can. If you've only got 15 minutes, running for that length of time is better than doing nothing at all. And longer sessions aren't always better. A 20-minute interval run will probably give you greater fitness benefits than plodding away at the same slow pace for 40 minutes.

## Take a break

Every few months, take a week off from running. This will give your body a chance to adapt to the stresses you have placed it under. During this break you could explore another sport, such as cycling, but keep your activity gentle to have a positive affect when you return to running.

## Warm up first thing

If you go out for a run shortly after waking up, it's even more important that you warm up properly because your muscles and tendons can shorten while you're asleep.

## Plan your intervals

You need to plan exactly what you're going to do in an interval session before you start. If you don't have a plan, it will be tempting to call it a day after only a few intervals. If you know you have to do a certain number, you're more likely to stick to your original interval target.

## Keep low on hills

Avoid taking a high knee lift on hills, because that wastes energy. The same goes for kicking your heels up at the back. Instead, try to glide up the slope.

## Use your hands off road

When you're running off road, you can use your hands to grab onto branches, so that you can drag yourself forwards or turn corners at speed without slipping over.

## Train with a partner

Running with someone else has a host of benefits. Having company can make cold winter runs more tolerable. Running partners are also good for forcing you to stick to sessions, because you're less likely to miss a run if it means letting someone down. Try to run with someone who is slightly better than you so that you can push yourself. But don't run with someone who is much better than you are as this can be demotivating.

# Race distance plans

## Use these plans to boost your fitness and get race ready

Following a plan will make it much easier to achieve your running goals than if you have no set agenda. Having your training mapped out allows you to enter runs in your diary, which means you're less likely to skip sessions.

A structured plan is designed to include a balance of runs that challenge your body and keep you motivated. They should include a range of sessions, such as speed, interval and long runs. It's also vital to factor in sufficient rest, so your body can recover and adapt to the training stimuli that make you improve.

These plans are based on the principle of progressive overload. When you start running, you are likely to make rapid improvement. But if you keep doing the same thing, that improvement will soon tail off. That's because you have to increase the challenge to your body if you want to continue improving your fitness. For example, by gradually increasing the distance of your long runs or the intensity or your interval sessions you'll put your body under new stress. Complementing that extra effort with well-timed rest days lets your body come back stronger than before.

If you're new to running, start by following the walk-to-run plan, which in just six weeks will take you from being a complete novice to being able to run solidly for half an hour. From there you can start tackling race distance plans, starting with a 5K programme and building up to a full marathon.

**Effort level**

Some of the sessions in these plans use an effort level from 1-10 to tell you how hard you should be working. Here's what the numbers mean:

**1-4** Easy up to a gentle jog
**5-6** Able to have a conversation
**6-7** Getting out of breath
**8-9** Can't talk, uncomfortable
**10** Flat out sprint

# Walk to run plan

## Go from complete novice to real runner in just six weeks

You're only six weeks away form being able to run non-stop for half an hour, even if you've never laced up a pair of running shoes before. Starting with small running intervals punctuated by substantial recovery periods is a more effective way for beginners to develop running fitness than jogging for as long as you can. You're exercising for half an hour from the first session, gradually building the length of runs and reducing the recoveries in each session. By the end of the plan, you'll be ready to move on to your first race training programme.

| ■ Week 1 | ■ Week 2 | ■ Week 3 | ■ Week 4 | ■ Week 5 | ■ Week 6 |
|---|---|---|---|---|---|
| **Monday**<br>Run 1 min, walk 2 mins, repeat 10 times | **Monday**<br>Run 2 mins, walk 2 mins, repeat 6 times | **Monday**<br>Run 3 mins, walk 3 mins, repeat 5 times | **Monday**<br>Run 6 mins, walk 3 mins, repeat 4 times | **Monday**<br>Run 8 mins, walk 2 mins, repeat 3 times | **Monday**<br>Run 12 mins, walk 2 mins, repeat 2 times |
| **Tuesday**<br>Rest | **Tuesday**<br>Rest | **Tuesday**<br>Rest | **Tuesday**<br>Rest | **Tuesday**<br>Rest | **Tuesday**<br>Rest |
| **Wednesday**<br>Run 1 min, walk 1 min, repeat 10 times | **Wednesday**<br>Run 2 mins, walk 2 mins, repeat 10 times | **Wednesday**<br>Run 3 mins, walk 2 mins, repeat 6 times | **Wednesday**<br>Run 6 mins, walk 2 mins, repeat 4 times | **Wednesday**<br>Run 10 mins, walk 2 mins, repeat 2 times | **Wednesday**<br>Run 15 mins, walk 2 mins, repeat 2 times |
| **Thursday**<br>Rest | **Thursday**<br>Rest | **Thursday**<br>Rest | **Thursday**<br>Rest | **Thursday**<br>Rest | **Thursday**<br>Rest |
| **Friday**<br>Rest | **Friday**<br>Rest | **Friday**<br>Rest | **Friday**<br>Rest | **Friday**<br>Rest | **Friday**<br>Rest |
| **Saturday**<br>Run 1 min, walk 1 min, repeat 15 times | **Saturday**<br>Run 2 mins, walk 1 min, repeat 10 times | **Saturday**<br>Run 5 mins, walk 3 mins, repeat 4 times | **Saturday**<br>Run 8 mins, walk 3 mins, repeat 3 times | **Saturday**<br>Run 20 mins | **Saturday**<br>Run 30 mins |
| **Sunday**<br>Rest | **Sunday**<br>Rest | **Sunday**<br>Rest | **Sunday**<br>Rest | **Sunday**<br>Rest | **Sunday**<br>Rest |

# 5K plan

## Follow this eight-week plan to beat your best, whatever your level

This plan is based on working at a rate of perceived exertion, which means you run according to your ability. If you're a first time racer and you've completed the walk to run plan on p45, this programme will give you a base of speed and endurance for you to complete the race in a time you can be proud of. If you're already a runner, you can use this speed-focused plan to push yourself and emerge with a personal best.

### ■ Week 1

**Monday**
20 minutes at level 8

**Tuesday**
Rest

**Wednesday**
20 minutes fartlek levels 5-9

**Thursday**
Rest

**Friday**
Rest

**Saturday**
4K level seven

**Sunday**
Rest

### ■ Week 2

**Monday**
20 minutes at level 8

**Tuesday**
Rest

**Wednesday**
20 minutes fartlek levels 5-9

**Thursday**
Rest

**Friday**
Rest

**Saturday**
5K level seven

**Sunday**
Rest

### ■ Week 3

**Monday**
25 minutes at level 8

**Tuesday**
Rest

**Wednesday**
25 minutes fartlek levels 5-9

**Thursday**
Rest

**Friday**
Rest

**Saturday**
6K level seven

**Sunday**
Rest

### ■ Week 4

**Monday**
25 minutes at level 8

**Tuesday**
Rest

**Wednesday**
25 minutes fartlek levels 5-9

**Thursday**
Rest

**Friday**
Rest

**Saturday**
7K level seven

**Sunday**
Rest

### ■ Week 5

**Monday**
30 minutes at level 8

**Tuesday**
Rest

**Wednesday**
30 minutes fartlek levels 5-9

**Thursday**
Rest

**Friday**
Rest

**Saturday**
7K level seven

**Sunday**
Rest

### ■ Week 6

**Monday**
30 minutes at level 8

**Tuesday**
Rest

**Wednesday**
30 minutes fartlek levels 5-9

**Thursday**
Rest

**Friday**
Rest

**Saturday**
8K level seven

**Sunday**
Rest

### ■ Week 7

**Monday**
25 minutes at level 8

**Tuesday**
Rest

**Wednesday**
25 minutes fartlek levels 5-9

**Thursday**
Rest

**Friday**
Rest

**Saturday**
5K level seven

**Sunday**
Rest

### ■ Week 8

**Monday**
Rest

**Tuesday**
20 mins at level 8

**Wednesday**
Rest

**Thursday**
20 mins at level 6

**Friday**
Rest

**Saturday**
Rest

**Sunday**
5K race

**Effort level**

Some of the sessions in these plans use an effort level from 1-10 to tell you how hard you should be working. Here's what the numbers mean:

**1-4** Easy up to a gentle jog
**5-6** Able to have a conversation
**6-7** Getting out of breath
**8-9** Can't talk, uncomfortable
**10** Flat out sprint

# 10K plan

## Build your speed endurance with this 12-week plan

One of the most popular races is 10K. It offers a great challenge to new runners and gives more experienced racers the chance to test their speed endurance. Each week of this plan includes a tempo session, where you push your maximum sustainable speed, an interval session, where you raise your lactate threshold, a short run to flush out the lactic acid and a long steady-state run to develop endurance. The first four weeks are where you build a solid base of running conditioning. The middle four weeks are where you up the distance and intensity, introducing structured intervals and actually completing the race distance. The final four weeks are where you hit peak intensity before tapering your training to ensure you're fresh and injury free for race day.

| ■ Week 1 | ■ Week 2 | ■ Week 3 | ■ Week 4 | ■ Week 5 | ■ Week 6 |
|---|---|---|---|---|---|
| **Monday**<br>20 mins at level 7 | **Monday**<br>20 mins at level 7 | **Monday**<br>25 mins at level 7 | **Monday**<br>25 mins at level 7 | **Monday**<br>30 mins at level 7 | **Monday**<br>30 mins at level 7 |
| **Tuesday**<br>Rest | **Tuesday**<br>Rest | **Tuesday**<br>Rest | **Tuesday**<br>Rest | **Tuesday**<br>Rest | **Tuesday**<br>Rest |
| **Wednesday**<br>3km fartlek, levels 5-9 | **Wednesday**<br>3km fartlek, levels 5-9 | **Wednesday**<br>4km fartlek, levels 5-9 | **Wednesday**<br>4km fartlek, levels 5-9 | **Wednesday**<br>5km fartlek, levels 5-9 | **Wednesday**<br>5km fartlek, levels 5-9 |
| **Thursday**<br>Rest | **Thursday**<br>Rest | **Thursday**<br>Rest | **Thursday**<br>Rest | **Thursday**<br>Rest | **Thursday**<br>Rest |
| **Friday**<br>3km at level 4 | **Friday**<br>3km at level 4 | **Friday**<br>4km at level 4 | **Friday**<br>4km at level 4 | **Friday**<br>5km at level 4 | **Friday**<br>5km at level 4 |
| **Saturday**<br>5km at level 7 | **Saturday**<br>6km at level 7 | **Saturday**<br>7km at level 7 | **Saturday**<br>8km at level 7 | **Saturday**<br>6km at level 7 | **Saturday**<br>7km at level 7 |
| **Sunday**<br>Rest | **Sunday**<br>Rest | **Sunday**<br>Rest | **Sunday**<br>Rest | **Sunday**<br>Rest | **Sunday**<br>Rest |

## Effort level

Some of the sessions in these plans use an effort level from 1-10 to tell you how hard you should be working. Here's what the numbers mean:

**1-4** Easy up to a gentle jog
**5-6** Able to have a conversation
**6-7** Getting out of breath
**8-9** Can't talk, uncomfortable
**10** Flat out sprint

| ■ Week 7 | ■ Week 8 | ■ Week 9 | ■ Week 10 | ■ Week 11 | ■ Week 12 |
|---|---|---|---|---|---|
| **Monday** 35 mins at level 7 | **Monday** 35 mins at level 7 | **Monday** 40 mins at level 7 | **Monday** 40 mins at level 7 | **Monday** 30 mins at level 7 | **Monday** 20 mins at level 7 |
| **Tuesday** Rest | **Tuesday** Rest | **Tuesday** Rest | **Tuesday** Rest | **Tuesday** Rest | **Tuesday** Rest |
| **Wednesday** Interval session: 2x800 metres, 2x400 metres, 2x200 metres, 2x100 metres, recover for half the interval distance | **Wednesday** Interval session: 2x100 metres, 2x200 metres, 2x400 metres, 2x800 metres, recover for half the interval distance | **Wednesday** Interval session: 5x1 min at level 9, recovering for four minutes between intervals. 5x100 metre sprints, recovering for 300 metres between intervals | **Wednesday** Interval session: 4x200 metres at level 9, 4x100 metres at level 9 or 10, 4x200 metres at level 9, 4x100 metres at level 9, recovering for 200 metres between all intervals | **Wednesday** 3km fartlek, level 5-9 | **Wednesday** Rest |
| **Thursday** Rest | **Thursday** Rest | **Thursday** Rest | **Thursday** Rest | **Thursday** Rest | **Thursday** 4km at level 4 |
| **Friday** 5km at level 4 | **Friday** 6km at level 4 | **Friday** 6km at level 4 | **Friday** 6km at level 4 | **Friday** 4km at level 4 | **Friday** Rest |
| **Saturday** 8km at level 7 | **Saturday** 10km at level 7 | **Saturday** 11km at level 7 | **Saturday** 12km at level 7 | **Saturday** 6km at level 7 | **Saturday** Rest |
| **Sunday** Rest | **Sunday** Rest | **Sunday** Rest | **Sunday** Rest | **Sunday** Rest | **Sunday** 10K race |

# Half marathon plan

## Start going long for a real test of endurance

A 21.1km (13.1 mile) half marathon is the perfect step between 10K events and a full marathon. It's a substantial test of fitness, but not one that makes huge demands on your time. Each week in this plan includes a tempo session where you push your maximum sustainable speed, an interval session where you raise your lactate threshold, a short easy run to flush out the lactic acid from your legs and a long steady-state run to develop endurance. The first four weeks are where you build a solid base of running conditioning. The middle four are where you up the distance and intensity, introducing structured intervals and entering a 10K race to give focus to your training. The final four weeks are where you should get close to completing the race distance before tapering your training substantially to make sure you're fresh and injury free for race day.

| ■ Week 1 | ■ Week 2 | ■ Week 3 | ■ Week 4 | ■ Week 5 | ■ Week 6 |
|---|---|---|---|---|---|
| **Monday**<br>20 mins at level 7 | **Monday**<br>20 mins at level 7 | **Monday**<br>25 mins at level 7 | **Monday**<br>25 mins at level 7 | **Monday**<br>30 mins at level 7 | **Monday**<br>30 mins at level 7 |
| **Tuesday**<br>Rest | **Tuesday**<br>Rest | **Tuesday**<br>Rest | **Tuesday**<br>Rest | **Tuesday**<br>Rest | **Tuesday**<br>Rest |
| **Wednesday**<br>4km fartlek, level 5-9 | **Wednesday**<br>4km fartlek, level 5-9 | **Wednesday**<br>5km fartlek, level 5-9 | **Wednesday**<br>5km fartlek, level 5-9 | **Wednesday**<br>Interval session: 2k at level 6, 5x1 min at level 8-9, recovering for three minutes between intervals. 2k at level 6 | **Wednesday**<br>6km at level 4 |
| **Thursday**<br>Rest | **Thursday**<br>Rest | **Thursday**<br>Rest | **Thursday**<br>Rest | **Thursday**<br>Rest | **Thursday**<br>Rest |
| **Friday**<br>4km at level 4 | **Friday**<br>5km at level 4 | **Friday**<br>6km at level 4 | **Friday**<br>6km at level 4 | **Friday**<br>6km at level 4 | **Friday**<br>Rest |
| **Saturday**<br>8km | **Saturday**<br>10km | **Saturday**<br>12km | **Saturday**<br>10km | **Saturday**<br>14km | **Saturday**<br>10K race |
| **Sunday**<br>Rest | **Sunday**<br>Rest | **Sunday**<br>Rest | **Sunday**<br>Rest | **Sunday**<br>Rest | **Sunday**<br>Rest |

## Effort level

Some of the sessions in these plans use an effort level from 1-10 to tell you how hard you should be working. Here's what the numbers mean:

**1-4** Easy up to a gentle jog
**5-6** Able to have a conversation
**6-7** Getting out of breath
**8-9** Can't talk, uncomfortable
**10** Flat out sprint

| ◼ Week 7 | ◼ Week 8 | ◼ Week 9 | ◼ Week 10 | ◼ Week 11 | ◼ Week 12 |
|---|---|---|---|---|---|
| **Monday** 35 mins at level 7 | **Monday** 35 mins at level 7 | **Monday** 40 mins at level 7 | **Monday** 40 mins at level 7 | **Monday** 30 mins at level 7 | **Monday** 20 mins at level 7 |
| **Tuesday** Rest | **Tuesday** Rest | **Tuesday** Rest | **Tuesday** Rest | **Tuesday** Rest | **Tuesday** Rest |
| **Wednesday** Interval session: 2km at level 6, 5x1 min at level 8-9, recovering for three minutes between intervals. 2km at level 6 | **Wednesday** Interval session: 2km at level 6, 5x2 mins at level 8-9, recovering for three minutes between intervals. 2km at level 6 | **Wednesday** Interval session: 2km at level 6, 5x2 mins at level 8-9, recovering for three minutes between intervals. 2km at level 6 | **Wednesday** Interval session: 2km at level 6, 5x1 min at level 8-9, recovering for three minutes between intervals. 2km at level 6 | **Wednesday** 4km fartlek, level 5-9 | **Wednesday** Rest |
| **Thursday** Rest | **Thursday** Rest | **Thursday** Rest | **Thursday** Rest | **Thursday** Rest | **Thursday** 4km at level 4 |
| **Friday** 6km at level 4 | **Friday** 6km at level 4 | **Friday** 6km at level 4 | **Friday** 5km at level 4 | **Friday** 4km at level 4 | **Friday** Rest |
| **Saturday** 14km | **Saturday** 17km | **Saturday** 20km | **Saturday** 14km | **Saturday** 8km | **Saturday** Rest |
| **Sunday** Rest | **Sunday** Rest | **Sunday** Rest | **Sunday** Rest | **Sunday** Rest | **Sunday** Half marathon race |

# Marathon plan

## Hit the big time with this 16-week guide to the ultimate distance

The marathon is the definitive running test for a recreational runner. It does require a large amount of training effort, but the satisfaction gained from completing the 26.2-mile (42.2km) course is well worth the exertion. Before you start this plan, you should have at least run a 10K race or, ideally, a half marathon because the plan assumes a good base level of fitness. Each week includes a tempo run to maintain your speed, as well as a fartlek session. If you're struggling to complete the runs, go easier during the intervals. You'll also do a medium-length easy run before your long weekend run, which is designed to build endurance. You should try to enter a half marathon once you're well into your plan to keep your training on track. It's also important to taper your training significantly in the final weeks to make sure you don't burn out before race day.

| ■ Week 1 | ■ Week 2 | ■ Week 3 | ■ Week 4 | ■ Week 5 | ■ Week 6 | ■ Week 7 | ■ Week 8 |
|---|---|---|---|---|---|---|---|
| **Monday** 20 mins at level 7 | **Monday** 20 mins at level 7 | **Monday** 25 mins at level 7 | **Monday** 25 mins at level 7 | **Monday** 30 mins at level 7 | **Monday** 30 mins at level 7 | **Monday** 35 mins at level 7 | **Monday** 35 mins at level 7 |
| **Tuesday** Rest | **Tuesday** Rest | **Tuesday** Rest | **Tuesday** Rest | **Tuesday** Rest | **Tuesday** Rest | **Tuesday** Rest | **Tuesday** Rest |
| **Wednesday** 4km fartlek, levels 5-9 | **Wednesday** 4km fartlek, levels 5-9 | **Wednesday** 5km fartlek, levels 5-9 | **Wednesday** 5km fartlek, levels 5-9 | **Wednesday** 6km fartlek, levels 5-9 | **Wednesday** 6km fartlek, levels 5-9 | **Wednesday** 10km at level 6 | **Wednesday** 2km at level 6, 4km fartlek at levels 5-9, 2km at level 6 |
| **Thursday** 6km at level 4 | **Thursday** 6km at level 4 | **Thursday** 8km at level 4 | **Thursday** 8km at level 4 | **Thursday** 10km at level 4 | **Thursday** 10km at level 4 | **Thursday** 12km at level 4 | **Thursday** 12km at level 4 |
| **Friday** Rest | **Friday** Rest | **Friday** Rest | **Friday** Rest | **Friday** Rest | **Friday** Rest | **Friday** Rest | **Friday** Rest |
| **Saturday** 14km | **Saturday** 16km | **Saturday** 18km | **Saturday** 21km | **Saturday** 16km | **Saturday** 19km | **Saturday** 22km | **Saturday** 25km |
| **Sunday** Rest | **Sunday** Rest | **Sunday** Rest | **Sunday** Rest | **Sunday** Rest | **Sunday** Rest | **Sunday** Rest | **Sunday** Rest |

## Effort level

Some of the sessions in these plans use an effort level from 1-10 to tell you how hard you should be working. Here's what the numbers mean:

**1-4** Easy up to a gentle jog
**5-6** Able to have a conversation
**6-7** Getting out of breath
**8-9** Can't talk, uncomfortable
**10** Flat out sprint

| ■ Week 9 | ■ Week 10 | ■ Week 11 | ■ Week 12 | ■ Week 13 | ■ Week 14 | ■ Week 15 | ■ Week 16 |
|---|---|---|---|---|---|---|---|
| **Monday** 35 mins at level 7 | **Monday** Rest | **Monday** 40 mins at level 7 | **Monday** 40 mins at level 7 | **Monday** 35 mins at level 7 | **Monday** 30 mins at level 7 | **Monday** 25 mins at level 7 | **Monday** 5km at level 4 |
| **Tuesday** Rest | **Tuesday** 10km level 6 | **Tuesday** Rest | **Tuesday** Rest | **Tuesday** Rest | **Tuesday** Rest | **Tuesday** Rest | **Tuesday** Rest |
| **Wednesday** 2km at level 6, 4km fartlek at levels 5-9, 2km at level 6 | **Wednesday** Rest | **Wednesday** 2km at level 6, 4km fartlek at levels 5-9, 2km at level 6 | **Wednesday** 10km at level 6 | **Wednesday** 2km at level 6, 4km fartlek at levels 5-9, 2km at level 6 | **Wednesday** 6km fartlek, levels 5-9 | **Wednesday** 4km fartlek, levels 5-9 | **Wednesday** Rest |
| **Thursday** Rest | **Thursday** 12km at level 4 | **Thursday** 10km at level 4 | **Thursday** 12km at level 4 | **Thursday** 12km at level 4 | **Thursday** 10km at level 4 | **Thursday** 8km at level 4 | **Thursday** 5km at level 4 |
| **Friday** Rest | **Friday** Rest | **Friday** Rest | **Friday** Rest | **Friday** Rest | **Friday** Rest | **Friday** Rest | **Friday** Rest |
| **Saturday** Half marathon race | **Saturday** 21km | **Saturday** 25km | **Saturday** 29km | **Saturday** 33km | **Saturday** 16km | **Saturday** 10km | **Saturday** Rest |
| **Sunday** Rest | **Sunday** Rest | **Sunday** Rest | **Sunday** Rest | **Sunday** Rest | **Sunday** Rest | **Sunday** Rest | **Sunday** Marathon race |

# Run the world

## Put your training to the test by entering the world's best races

### Top 10 UK races

**Exe to Axe, March**
This 20-mile (32.2km) fell course along the Jurassic coast in Devon from Exmouth to Seaton is a real test of stamina and endurance. Runners must climb in excess of 1,300 metres during the scenic race. Most of the major hills are late on, but the winds are constant.
**sidmouthrunningclub.org.uk**

**London Marathon, April**
The most famous marathon in the world is also one of the largest with more than 36,000 runners taking part each year. Every one of the 42.2km from start to finish draws huge crowds and the atmosphere can be a big motivator.
**london-marathon.co.uk**

London Marathon

**Chedworth Roman Trail 10, April**
A challenging 10-mile (16.1km) cross-country race through the uneven yet stunning footpaths and fields of the Cotswold countryside around the Chedworth Roman villa estate. The tough terrain also features several steep hills and a knee-deep crossing of the Churn river.
**cirencester-ac.org.uk**

**Keep Your Eye On the Ball 5K, June**
This football-themed 5K race through London's Victoria park is organised by the Everyman male cancer research campaign. It pits football supporters from across the UK against each other for the accolade of the country's fastest fans; great fun and ideal for beginners.
**icr.ac.uk/everyman**

**British 10K London, July**
Starting on Piccadilly, the British 10K takes in some of central London's most historic and iconic landmarks, such as Trafalgar Square and St. Paul's Cathedral. This is a fairly flat course but get to the front if you want to post a good time.
**thebritish10klondon.co.uk**

**Swansea Bay 10K, September**
Set alongside the Swansea coast, this flat and straight 10K course is perfect for shaving seconds off a personal best. Other distances, including a 5K and 3K, are also on offer. With many of the world's elite runners making the trip to south Wales, the event is one of the most popular road races in Britain.
**swanseabay10k.com**

**Run to the Beat, October**
The 21.1km run is London's first official half marathon. Organisers will blast out motivational live music from strategic points along the route, which starts and finishes at the O2 Arena. The race's resident sports scientist says the tunes can make your run seem ten per cent easier.
**runtothebeat.co.uk**

**Great North Run, October**
The Great North Run is the world's most popular half marathon with nearly 50,000 runners taking part in the annual 21.1km course that snakes through Newcastle-upon-Tyne and South Shields. This is another race that benefits from a buzzing atmosphere.
**greatrun.org**

**Loch Ness Marathon, October**
One of the UK's most scenic marathons, the course follows a spectacular journey through rugged Highland scenery and along the south-eastern shores of Loch Ness before finishing inside the Inverness Queens Park Stadium.
**lochnessmarathon.com**

**Saab Salomon Turbo-X, November**
This a gruelling multi-terrain event that weaves along water-logged tracks and trails that are frequently interrupted by steep hills. The testing course is about 11 miles (17.7km) but feels much longer.
**saabsalomontrails.co.uk**

Saab Salomon Turbo-X

The Great North Run is the world's biggest half marathon

# Top 10 international races

### Dubai Marathon, January
The world's richest race offers millions of dollars of prize money to any athlete who can post a world record. That's probably a bit beyond your reach but you do get close to financial excess by following the route that runs past the exotic resorts of the Jumeriah Road with the halfway point marked by the Burj Al Arab – the world's only seven-star hotel. A 10K race is also run.
**dubaimarathon.org**

### Lisbon Half Marathon, March
The pancake-flat course makes this one of world's fastest half marathons and a firm favourite for those chasing a personal best. With a unique start – halfway along the Portuguese capital's oldest bridge – and a course that hugs the Tagus river, it's easy to see why 30,000 runners enter every year.
**lisbon-half-marathon.com**

**Lisbon Half Marathon**

### Marathon des Sables, March
In this event, billed as the toughest foot race in the world, runners must tackle 251km – the equivalent of six marathons – in just six days across the scorching sands of the Moroccan desert. Each day varries in length, with the longest leg a determination testing 84km. To make it even harder, competitors must carry all the supplies they need for the entire event in a backpack with only water and tents provided at checkpoints.
**darbaroud.com**

### Berlin Runs... 25km, May
Founded by French forces in West Berlin back in 1981, this is Germany's longest-running road race. It takes in some of the capital's most impressive landmarks such as the Brandenburg Gate and Potsdamer Square before finishing on the running track of the Olympic Stadium, which hosted the 1972 games.
**berlin-laeuft.de**

### Midnight Sun Marathon, June
Held in the Norwegian city of Tromsø, at 70 latitude and 350km inside the Arctic Circle, this is one of the world's northernmost marathons and provides a unique opportunity to run through the picturesque landscape in bright sunlight despite the starting gun firing late at night.
**msm.no**

### Victoria Falls Marathon, August
With a starting point in the shadow of the world's tallest waterfall, the Victoria Falls marathon is one of Africa's newest, and most scenic, races. The course also incorporates parts of the Zambezi national park, which is home to elephants, lions and crocodiles, which probably helps runners meet the five-and-a-half hours cut-off time for receiving a medal.
**vicfallsmarathon.com**

### Sydney City2Surf, August
This 14km race from the heart of Sydney to the world-famous Bondi beach is Australia's biggest road race and regularly attracts more than 60,000 runners, most of them bronzed and scarily athletic. It is a hilly course throughout and one of the few events that attracts more female than male entrants.
**city2surf.sunherald.com.au**

### Dublin Marathon, October
Good news for runners chasing a fast time; this is a very flat course. The start and finish is close to the city centre so you don't have far to stagger after the race for a celebratory pint of Guinness. It's also a great race for first timers. Dubbed the 'friendly marathon', lively support from the crowds will help to spur you on through those last few painful miles.
**dublincitymarathon.ie**

### New York City Marathon, November
The Big Apple is home to the world's largest marathon with nearly 40,000 runners taking in the sights and sounds of the city's five boroughs from the start on Staten Island to the finish along Fifth Avenue into Central Park in Manhattan. Make sure you leave some energy in the tank because the last few miles involve a few hills.
**nycmarathon.org**

### Las Vegas Marathon, December
The only race that offers runners views of the Eiffel Tower, the Statue of Liberty and Caesar's Palace all within the same glance, the Sin City marathon follows the highways that border the Nevada desert. It's generally a bit more colourful than your average marathon, with plenty of Elvis impersonators taking part. The course also features a run-through wedding chapel, should you wish to get hitched mid-race.
**lvmarathon.com**

**Las Vegas Marathon**

The City2Surf race in Sydney runs from the town to the beach

# Key running terms

### ■ Aerobic

Aerobic (meaning 'with air') exercise requires oxygen intake to fuel muscles for prolonged periods of activity, such as distance running.

### ■ Anaerobic

During anaerobic (meaning 'without air') exercise, the body's requirement for energy exceeds that provided by respiration. Without oxygen, a muscle's ability to perform is dramatically reduced and can only function for short intensive bursts.

### ■ Cool-down

A period of low-intensity exercise and stretching that lasts between five and 15 minutes, and is done after a session of more intense exercise. It aids the body's transition back to a resting state by lowering the heart rate and regulating breathing. It also flushes out lactic acid to aid muscle recovery.

### ■ Cushioned shoe

These have the least added stability of all specialist running shoes and are designed for high-arched feet that don't overpronate.

### ■ Delayed onset muscle soreness

Muscular pain that is felt between 24 and 72 hours after exercise, and which usually subsides after two or three days. Microscopic muscle tears are thought responsible. Downhill running can exacerbate the problem.

### ■ Dynamic stretch

Controlled body movements, such as arm and leg swings and torso twists, that gently and gradually take the muscles to the limit of their range of motion. Usually performed as part of a **warm-up** before a run.

### ■ Fartlek

Meaning 'speed play' in Swedish. A form of **interval training** where running speed is alternated between easy, medium and hard during a single session. It works the cardiovascular system harder than a session in which a constant speed is maintained.

### ■ Footstrike

The first part of the foot, either heel, midfoot or the toes, that makes contact with the ground to begin the **gait cycle**.

### ■ Gait cycle

This begins when one foot strikes the ground and ends when it makes contact again having completed one stride.

### ■ Interval training

Alternating periods of high-speed and high-intensity exercise with low-intensity recovery exercise. It provides greater cardiovascular gains than maintaining a constant pace.

### ■ Lactic acid

A chemical compound of carbon, hydrogen, and oxygen that forms in hard-working muscles. If levels become too high, results in performance can deteriorate.

### ■ Midsole

A layer of foam cushioing in the sole between the **outsole** and the **upper**.

### ■ Motion-control shoe

Designed for runners who **overpronate**, usually as a result of having feet with low or flat arches.

### ■ Outsole

The bottom part of a shoe that provides traction and reduces wear on the **midsole**, which is responsible for providing much of the shoe's cushioning.

### ■ Overpronation

When the foot strikes the ground first on the outside of the heel and consequently rolls inwards as the foot lands fully and then takes off. Requires **motion-control** or high-stability shoes to prevent injuries.

### ■ Overtraining

Occurs when exercise volume or intensity is greater than recovery capacity. It can lead to a loss of fitness and strength rather than continued progress.

### ■ Stability shoe

An all-round shoe, offering a good level of cushioning. Best suited to runners with an average foot arch – where the feet land and roll forwards, efficiently absorbing shock. These runners do not need shoes that offer additional support or cushioning.

### ■ Static stretch

The gradual lengthening of a muscle at rest to the point of discomfort. The stretch is held for between 10 and 30 seconds to improve the muscle's range of motion. Should be done after, rather than before, a run.

### ■ Tempo run

A run typically lasting less than an hour, performed at a controlled, moderately fast pace where brief conversation should just be possible. Designed to improve running efficiency and speed.

### ■ Trail shoe

Provides additional traction and protection for running on unstable terrain. Trail shoes often have less cushioning than road trainers and position the feet closer to the ground for extra stability.

### ■ Upper

The part of the shoe above the sole that covers your feet.

### ■ Wicking

A type of fabric that moves sweat from the skin to the outer layer of clothing, where it evaporates, leaving the fabric dry.

### ■ Warm-up

A period of low-intensity exercise and stretching, typically lasting between five and 15 minutes and done before a session of more intense exercise. It helps prepare the body and mind for exercise by slowly warming up the muscles and increasing heart rate.

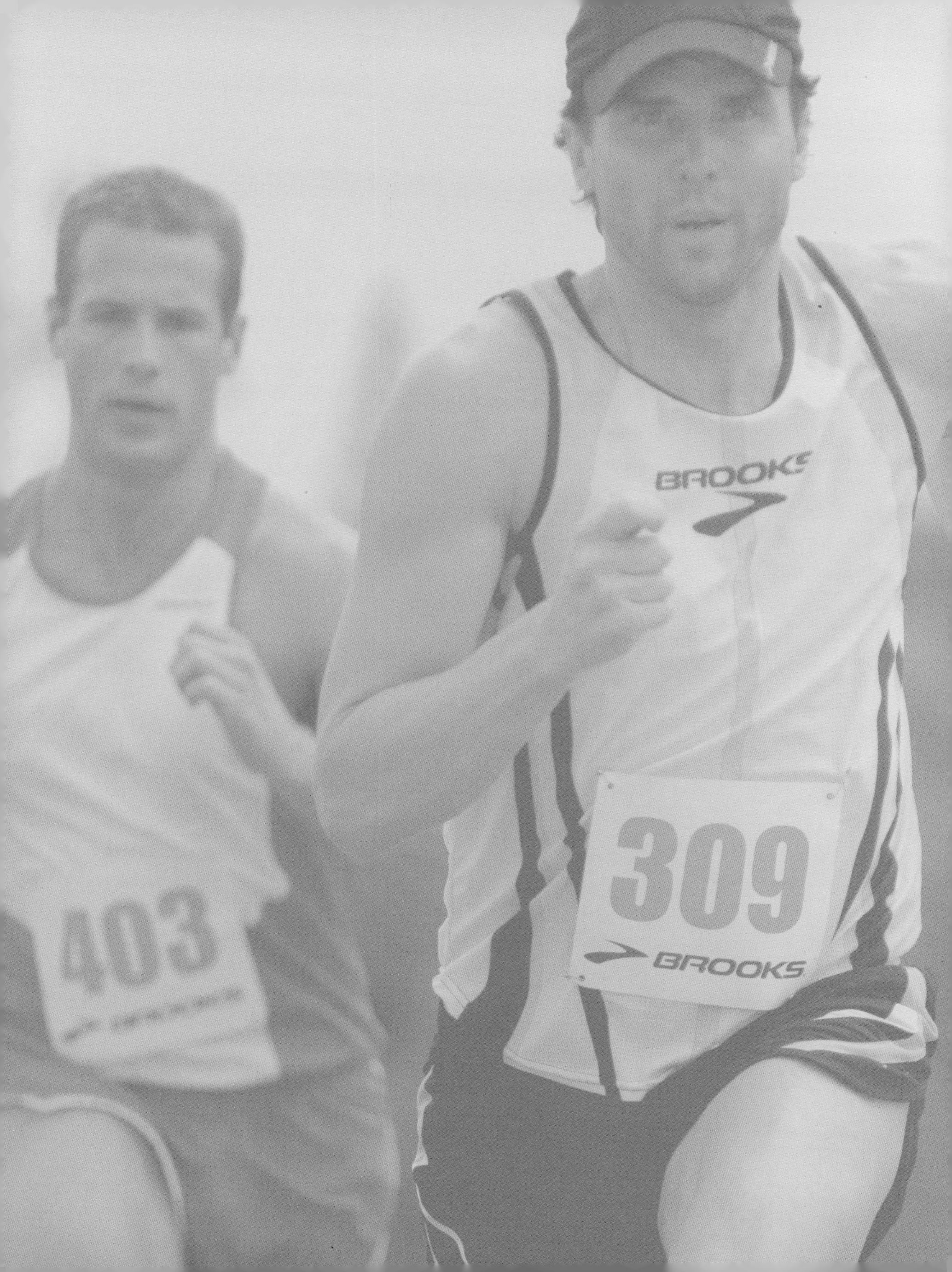
BROOKS
309
BROOKS
403

# part 2

# Bike

Boost your road cycling speed
and endurance with our comprehensive
gear, technique and training advice

# Hit the road

## Enjoy the thrill of road cycling and get fit in the saddle

You probably cycled a lot as a kid and, as the saying goes, you never forget how to ride a bike. That may be true, but back then you probably weren't worrying about fork rake (how much forward bend there is in the forks connecting the frame to the front wheel), warming up properly or taking part in interval training sessions. That's where this section can help, because if you want to cycle for fitness you need the right kit and a structured training regime. The following pages will give you all the information and advice you need to get fit in the saddle.

### How to use this section

These days, road bikes are finely crafted machines. The shape, weight and durability of each bike part is specially selected to suit a particular style of riding. The Gear pages (p64-71) detail the main attributes of a standard road bike, a racing bike and a touring bike built for longer, slower rides. They also show you how to set up your bike so you can ride it efficiently. Later in the chapter you'll learn how to look after and maintain your shiny new bit of kit.

At a basic level, cycling is a relatively straightforward sport, but you can adjust your cadence (pedal speed), body position and the way you exert force on the pedals to improve your riding, and that's explored in the Technique pages in this section.

Once you have mastered pedal revolution, and warmed up properly (p76-77), it's time to start thinking about different types of ride. The Training Methods section outlines the key options that will allow you to build long rides, speed sessions and hill climbing into your routine for a rounded training effect.

The more power you're able to exert and the more stability you have in your joints and muscles, the faster you'll be able to ride. Time in the saddle is good at developing some cycling muscles, such as the quads, but it's less suited to developing core stability. Follow our power and stability workouts (p80-85) and you'll get in the right condition to make real progress.

Put all this together and you're ready to start following one of the four riding plans. They kick off with one aimed at beginners, which establishes a base level of fitness. It is followed by programmes that will prepare you for short (50 mile) and longer (100 mile) cyclosportive races, as well as a time-trial race. We've also picked the ten best cyclosportive races that you should enter to put your new skills and fitness to the test.

## Benefits of cycling

### ■ It's easy on your joints

Once your bike is set up correctly, cycling places very little strain on your joints, even though it involves a repetitive action. This means you can train hard without dramatically increasing your injury risk. So, providing you have a sound technique and allow enough recovery between hard riding sessions, cycling can give you fast fitness gains because you can complete a large volume of work at a comparatively early stage of your training. This should also give you an extra motivational boost.

### ■ It's great for weight loss

Cycling burns, on average, around 800 calories per hour when riding at 16-19 miles per hour on the flat. That's one of the highest calorie-burn values of any sport and the weight loss potential of cycling can be increased by other factors. Because your weight is being carried by the bike, long rides can be undertaken by relatively inexperienced cyclists, and the longer you ride the more calories you burn. Riding uphill in a challenging gear will also burn lots of calories.

### ■ You can target fast twitch muscle fibres

Steady rides, which target the slow twitch muscle fibres responsible for creating lean-looking muscles, are great for improving stamina. Fast twitch fibres are thicker, and hitting them hard in a workout builds power and adds shape and size to your muscles. Sprinting on the flat or climbing hills in short all-out bursts, activates your fast twitch fibres. As long as you warm up properly, you can hit them hard without putting undue strain on your joints.

# Anatomy of a road bike

Designed for speed and frequent use, road bikes give you both comfort and performance

## ■ Saddle

Comfort, support and good anatomical design are more important than weight.

## ■ Frame

The main frame is made from welded tubes, which are custom designed in shape, diameter and tube wall thickness to fit a specific place on the frame. These design refinements keep weight to a minimum while accommodating the different stresses that act on different parts of the frame.

## ■ Seat stays

These can be made from either carbon fibre, steel or aluminium. Carbon fibre seat stays increase riding comfort by absorbing some energy from road bumps.

## ■ Chainset

The smaller chainrings of a compact chainset, in this case 50 and 34 teeth, combined with a wide spread of different sized sprockets on the rear wheel, provide a wide range of gear ratios, including very low ones for easier riding up steep hills.

## ■ Tyres

Fat tyres give a more comfortable ride than thin ones. Puncture-proof layers within the tyre make them more dependable.

## ■ Head tube

A long head tube gives a higher handlebar position, which means a more upright riding position. This places less stress on your arm, shoulder, back and neck muscles. It also gives good vision for riding in traffic.

## ■ Pedals

A matter of personal choice. Clipless pedals are the best, but on a bike like this you could use racing clipless pedals or off-road/touring clipless pedals. Racing pedals require special shoes that are quite difficult to walk in. Off-road/touring clipless pedals still require dedicated cycling shoes, but walking in them is much easier.

## ■ Handlebars and stem

Handlebars are often made from aluminium for lightness. Stems tend to be shorter than on race bikes to provide an upright and comfortable riding position.

## ■ Forks

Carbon fibre forks absorb bumps and vibrations better than aluminium ones and are just as light. This bike has further vibration damping from elastic polymer inserts within the fork legs.

**Specialized Allez Elite 2008 road bike, £799.99**

---

## Bike kit

### Essential protection for every rider

**■ Helmet**
Ensure that the helmet has passed a recognised safety standard. Ventilation slots will keep you cool. It should fit so that when moved slightly your scalp moves with it. Wear it straight and level, with the front four to six centimetres above your eyes.
**Pictured: Giro Atmos road helmet, £99.99**

**■ Gloves**
Special fingerless cycling gloves soak up sweat, give good grip on the handlebars and protect your hands in the event of a fall. They should fit closely and have smooth seams.
**Pictured: Altura Craig Mitt, £6.99**

**■ Lights**
Front and rear lights, plus a rear reflector, are compulsory by law when riding a bike in the dark in Britain. LEDs, both constant and flashing, are best for a rear light. Lights with high-power bulbs that illuminate the road are best up front.
**Pictured: Cat Eye EL520/LD610 light set, £49.99**

All products available from Evans Cycles, evanscycles.com

# Anatomy of a racing bike

Built for maximun speed, racing bikes are
a high-tech and lightweight option

## ■ Head tube
A short head tube means
lower handlebars and
riding position, increasing
rider aerodynamics.

## ■ Saddle
Made from materials such
as titanium, light plastics
and even carbon fibre,
race saddles sacrifice a
little comfort to provide a
light, firm platform from
which to pedal.

## ■ Frame
Often made from carbon fibre tubes, a
material picked for its high strength-to-
weight ratio but sometimes built from
steel or aluminium. The tubes are formed
from sheets of woven carbon fibre, where
the sheets' properties and weave direction
are chosen specifically for each tube..

## ■ Chainset
Usually made from either carbon fibre
or aluminium. Large chainrings, in this
case 53 and 39 teeth, give the higher
gears needed to cope with the speed
of road racing

## ■ Tyres
Narrow tyres improve
aerodynamics and their small
road footprint reduces friction.
Puncture-protection layers
within their construction are
made from supple materials,
such as Kevlar, which don't
detract from the rolling
properties. Thin and very
supple tyre walls reduce
rolling resistance still further.

### ■ Handlebars and stem

Carbon fibre reduces weight and increases stiffness, as well as absorbing some road vibrations. Handlebars are often wing shaped at the top for improved aerodynamics.

### ■ Wheels

Drag on spokes is high because they move through the air at the combined speed of the bike and the revolution of the wheel. Fewer spokes means less drag, as do spokes with a flattened profile. Also, fewer spokes combined with light alloy metals make for light wheels, which are easier to accelerate.

### ■ Forks

Fork legs and the steerer can be made from carbon fibre. The steerer is the tube that fits inside the head tube and connects to the handlebars. The total carbon construction helps to keep weight to a minimum.

Bianchi B4P 928 Carbon T-TUBE 10 speed Chorus 2008 road bike, £2,699.99

## Bike kit

### Essential speed wear for every rider

#### ■ Top

Wear a breathable base layer – thermal for winter and a thin material in summer. Short-sleeved cycling tops with rear pockets are for summer. Long-sleeved and thermal tops complete your winter cycling wardrobe.
**Pictured: Altura Asymmetrix short sleeved jersey, £39.99**

#### ■ Cycling shorts

Baggy or lycra is a matter of choice, but all cycling shorts should have a seat insert to prevent chaffing. Check it – if it feels rough or has loose stitching in the shop, it will bite you where it hurts when you are riding. Cycling tights are for riding in really cold weather.
**Pictured: Nike baggy shorts, £34.99**

#### ■ Shoes

Cycling shoes have stiff soles with cleats on them that engage and disengage easily with clipless pedals. Cleats ensure good contact with the pedals, transferring power from your legs throughout each pedal revolution.
**Pictured: Shimano R131 SPD-SL shoe, £89.99**

#### ■ Sunglasses

A must in summer – not just for looking cool, but for keeping the sun, flies and dust out of your eyes. Get a pair with interchangeable lenses, so you have a clear option for dull days, and yellow lenses to brighten dark winter days.
**Pictured: Specialized San Remo Adaptalite, £74.99**

All products available from Evans Cycles, evanscycles.com

# Anatomy of a touring bike

Touring bikes are comfortable workhorses that will get you through long, loaded rides

### ■ Frame
Steel alloys are good all-round materials for touring frames. Other materials might be stronger, lighter or more rigid, but steel combines all of these properties. It also gives a comfortable ride, which makes it ideal for cycle touring. Steel offers a relatively cheap option for a custom-built frame, too.

### ■ Saddle
Comfort is everything when you are touring. This saddle is made from leather, which over time and with proper care moulds its shape to yours.

### ■ Pannier racks
These fit on the rear and, sometimes, the front of touring bikes. They support pannier bags for carrying clothing, food, and even a tent and full camping kit for real adventure cycle touring.

### ■ Mudguards
These protect you from standing water and mud on the roads and make riding much more comfortable. They also keep your clothes clean, an important consideration on a multi-day tour when you're carrying all of your gear with you.

### ■ Wheels.
Speed is of less importance than strength and comfort. Wheels have plenty of spokes for strength. Wide rims accommodate fat tyres for comfort.

### ■ Rear mech
Large sprockets and small chainrings give low gears for steep hills. Small sprockets and large chainrings are for fast riding. The wide range of gear ratios requires a longer drive chain and a mountain bike-style rear mech to keep chain tension constant.

**■ Forks**

Fork rake is a measure of how much forward bend there is in the fork legs. Touring bikes have a large fork rake to absorb shock and increase stability when cornering with fully-loaded pannier bags.

**■ Chainset**

Triple chainsets have three chainrings, with the bigger two for general riding and the smallest providing the ultra-low gear ratios required for taking a fully-loaded bike into hilly country.

**■ Pedals**

Dual-sided pedals are adaptable. One side takes the cleat of a clipless pedal cycling shoe, and the other is a simple platform suitable for normal shoes.

**■ Brakes**

Cantilever brakes similar to those you find on some mountain bikes give good stopping power for a heavily-laden touring bike. They also create space in which to fit wide mudguards.

Dawes Ultra Galaxy touring bike, £999.99

---

## Bike kit

### Essential extras for every rider

**■ Tool kit**

A multi-tool – something like a Swiss Army Knife but with Allen keys and screwdrivers instead of blades and scissors – three tyre levers and spare inner tubes.
**Pictured: Topeak Alien 2 tool, £32.99**

**■ Inner tube**

Take a couple of spare inner tubes. Trying to fiddle about with a repair kit, espcially in hot weather, is too difficult to be practical. You'll need to take a good-quality bike pump, too.
**Pictured: Bontrager inner tube, £4.99**

**■ Hydration devices**

Bladder hydration systems are good if you are into really long rides. Make sure you, get a cycling-specific system. Plastic bottles that fit into a frame-mounted cage are still the best option. You can fit two cages on most bikes.
**Pictured: Camelback Octane 8+, £79.99**

**■ Cycle computers**

There's nothing like knowing how far and how fast you've ridden to give you satisfaction and the motivation to do more. There are handlebar-mounted devices available that record anything from basic information to data on altitude, calories used, heart rate and power output.
**Pictured: Polar CS600 cycling computer, £474.99**

All products available from Evans Cycles, evanscycles.com

# How to set up your bike

Setting up your bike correctly will give you maximum speed for your efforts. Make these adjustments before you go out for your first ride

### ■ Seat height

Remove your shoes, get on your bike and place your heel over the pedal axle. Push that pedal to the bottom of the pedal revolution. Your leg should be almost straight. Do not lean over to favour that leg. Loosen the seat pin clamp bolt and raise or lower the saddle until it is in a position where your leg is almost straight. Check both legs, and if one is shorter go for the near straight position on the shorter leg.

### ■ Seat position

Sit on your bike with your cycling shoes engaged in the pedals and turn the cranks until they are parallel to the floor. The slight indentation outside and behind the kneecap of your forward leg should be directly over the pedal axle. A helper is best to judge this. Loosen the bolt under the saddle and move the saddle backwards or forwards until you get the knee indentation over the pedal axle.

## ■ Seat angle

Your seat should be flat. Lay a spirit level across the length of the saddle after setting your seat position and before you tighten the saddle bolt. Check again after the bolt is tight because tightening can alter the angle. If it has moved, loosen the bolt, adjust the angle accordingly and re-tighten.

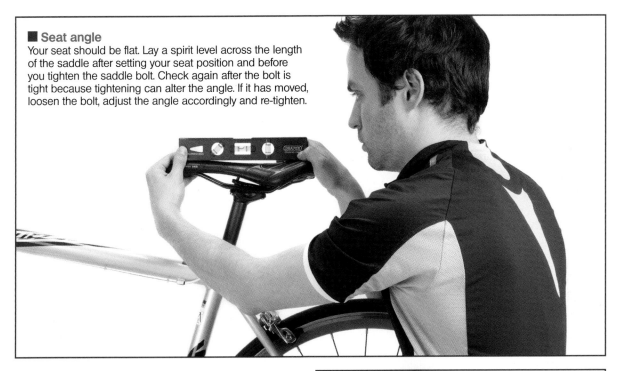

## ■ Foot position

The cleats on your cycling shoe determine foot position. You should pedal with the widest part of your foot (which is just behind your little toe) directly over the pedal axle. To set up your cleats, mark where the widest part of your foot is on the outside of your cycling shoes, then draw a line from the mark across the sole of each shoe from the outside to the inside. Line up the shoe cleat so that the middle of the cleat is directly over this line, then tighten the cleat screws.

## ■ Handlebar position

Handlebar height is matter of personal choice and a factor of the type of cycling you do, but they should never be so low that your knees hit your chest. A higher handlebar position is more comfortable, but less aerodynamic. Handlebars should be angled so that brake levers can be easily operated from above and below.

# The perfect revolution

There's more to cycling than jumping on your bike and pedalling furiously. Here's some advice to make your riding more efficicent

## Cadence

The number of revolutions you complete in one minute (cadence) is the key to efficient pedalling. When seven-time Tour de France winner Lance Armstrong returned to training after suffering from cancer, his coach came up with a new training method to reduce muscle fatigue and speed recovery. The approach was to lower the gear and increase cadence. The legs move faster under less resistance, so the cardiovascular system has to work harder but the muscles undergo less severe contractions. The result is that they get less fatigued, allowing them to pedal for longer and recover quicker. For novices, anything between 90-100 revolutions per minute (rpm) on the flat is the most efficient work rate for both burning calories and training aerobically.

## Pedal power

Power isn't just about spinning your pedals round in a blur. To maximise efficiency, you need to think about how and when you apply pressure to the pedal. Riders produce most of their power on the downstroke, so this is where you should concentrate your effort. Power output falls as the pedals go though the top and bottom of the stroke. The force of the downstroke also virtually negates the opposite leg's ability to produce any power on the upstroke. You can get around this by learning to apply force through as much of the stroke as possible, particularly through the top and bottom. To practice, try a high-powered session where you go up a hill in a high gear in a low cadence while staying in the

saddle. This will force you to keep power flowing to the pedals over the top and through the bottom of the stroke because it's the only way you can keep moving.

## Posture

Good posture will help you to transfer power efficiently to the pedals so focus on your postural muscles in your core and pelvis. Rather than getting your legs to do all the work, you should keep your hips aligned with the bike and contract your core muscles to let the power flow through your body into the pedals. You should avoid rocking your hips at all costs. Also, if your saddle is too high, that will force you to rock from side to side to compensate for not being able to reach the pedals.

## Out of the saddle

When standing up on the pedals, you should keep your shoulders level, contract your core and pull on the handlebars just enough to stabilise your body. When you come out of the

saddle, your power comes from your core and pelvic muscles, so tense your glutes and core just as you would do when lifting something heavy.

## Cornering

You're aiming to maintain your speed without skidding and coming off your bike. Go into the corner wide, cut in at the shortest line and come out wide. Lean slightly into the corner, lift up your inside knee and put your weight on your outside handlebar to balance your weight against your momentum. Look at where you want to come out and your bike should follow. To avoid crashing, brake before rather than in the corner and accelerate hard out of the corner. For very tight corners, such as hairpin bends, you'll have to drop your speed.

## Hills

When you hit a hill, your natural instinct is to push as hard as you can in the gear you're already in. But the most efficient way to get up a hill is to change down into a lower gear and keep the cadence at 90-100rpm. It's important to try to get into a rhythm. Some people like to sit, others like to stand. It depends on the athlete. Drafting doesn't work on hills and you can forget about aerodynamics unless you're going really fast. On descents, relax your body and, if it's a long downhill, turn your legs over every so often to prevent them from stiffening up. You can reduce your speed by making your body position less aerodynamic, as well as applying the brakes.

# Position of strength

Follow these form pointers
to perfect your technique

■ The flatter your back the more
aerodynamic your position, but only
flatten it if you're comfortable. If you're
uncomfortable with a flat back, you won't
be able to sustain the position.

■ Your hips should stay level when
you're pedalling rather than rocking
from side to side.

■ You can switch between standing
and sitting during longer climbs to
transfer the load between muscle
groups.

■ Keep your knees in line with the
pedals. This transfers force in the
most efficient way

■ Maintain a smooth, constant pedal
stroke. Your heels should drive your
feet during each stroke. It's the most
efficient way of exerting power. You
can develop that by riding using only
one leg.

■ Hold a straight line on the road by focusing on a point 20 metres in front of you.

■ You need a definite bend in your elbow to make sure you transfer all your weight to your legs. Locking out the upper body helps ensure that your effort comes from your legs.

■ Change your hand position regularly during long rides to avoid tensing up in your arms and shoulders.

■ The widest part of your foot should be in line with the pedal axle. Pushing the pedals with your toes or the arch of your foot isn't efficient.

# Warming up

Start your session with a proper warm-up and you'll feel better, ride faster and last longer

It's essential that you do a proper warm-up before a ride. Warming up will raise your core temperature and prepare your muscles for the work to come. By doing some gentle cycling, you make your heart beat faster, which pumps oxygen and nutrients to your muscles and elevates your body's core temperature. Warm muscles are more elastic, so you can work them through their full range of motion with less chance of injury. Warming up is particularly important if you're going straight into a high-intensity session.

### Pre-ride warm-up

■ Start by riding slowly and gradually increase the pace until your heart rate has reached 80 per cent of it's maximum.

■ Once your heart rate has been raised, perform some dynamic stretches, such as the ones outlined on p25.

■ Get back on your bike and get your heart rate back up to about 80 per cent, holding it there for five minutes before starting the main body of your session.

■ Some coaches recommend doing short, flat-out sprints at the end of your warm-up, although recent scientific studies have questioned whether this improves performance.

# Cooling down

## End your ride in the right way to speed up recovery

Cooling down after a ride will lower your heart rate and help flush lactic acid out of your muscles so you can recover quickly. Spend the last five to ten minutes of your session bringing your heart rate back down by pedalling in an easy gear, then do the stretches below.

### Post-ride stretches

Static stretches relax your muscles, which are then held under tension for a period of time without moving. This helps to lengthen your muscles and is particularly helpful for cycling, which, if done regularly, can cause tightness in the quads and shorten your hamstrings. The stretches shown on p30-31 will help loosen the muscles that frequently tighten up during a ride. You'll also need to add upper-body stretches, which are shown below, to your routine. Get into the stretch position and allow your muscles to relax. As you place pressure on the muscle you should be able to feel it relaxing and lengthening. You can slowly increase the pressure on the muscle throughout the duration of the stretch, but never force it or 'bounce' because that can damage the muscle. If you feel pain, stop immediately.

### Upper-back stretch

Stand with your arms extended in front of you, your fingers interwoven and your palms facing away from you. Gently push your hands away from your body until you feel the stretch. Hold that position for 20 seconds, then repeat three times.

### Lower-back stretch

Keeping your shoulders flat on the floor, bend one knee at 90° and rotate your hips to send that leg over your other leg. Press down on your bent knee until you feel a stretch. Hold that position for 20 seconds and repeat twice on both sides.

### Traps stretch

If you're in the saddle for a long time, your traps can tighten up. To stretch them out, pull gently on your head and pull your opposite shoulder down. Hold that position for 20 seconds and repeat twice on both sides.

# Performance enhancers

## Apply a range of training methods to your rides to boost your fitness

Riding at one pace, even if it's a very fast pace, won't give you all the benefits you can get from cycling. That doesn't mean you should avoid steady-state rides completely. You need them to lay down a solid foundation to your training. Once you've done that, you can introduce rides at your anaerobic threshold and speed sessions to hit your fast-twitch muscles. Hill repetitions provide you with further leg and lung-testing training sessions.

### Steady-state rides
Cycling at a constant pace, where you can still get whole sentences out between taking breaths, increases the number of blood capillaries in your muscles and the number of cells in them that produce energy. It also increases the volume of your heart. The net result is that more oxygen and fuel is made available for your muscles. A concerted period of steady-state riding should be done before moving on to harder work. Sessions at this level must still be included along with more advanced training to maintain the adaptations made.

### Interval training
Intervals are repetitions of harder riding separated by periods at an easier pace. The idea behind separating hard riding with easier sections is that it allows you to do more riding in total at a target hard pace than if you tried to ride at that pace without resting.

Intervals are the cornerstone of getting fitter on your bike. Once you have a good base of steady riding

under your belt, doing intervals will push up your anaerobic threshold (the point at which your body cannot keep up with lactic acid build up). Start with three intervals of six minutes separated by four minutes easy, and build to three or four intervals of ten minutes.

After you get used to threshold intervals, add shorter intervals of three to five minutes going as hard as you can for that time, separated by equal periods of easy riding. This will improve

your capacity to ride hard and your tolerance of lactic acid.

Short intervals of 30 seconds to two minutes in a high gear with easier periods of equal length are one of the best ways of putting raw power into your pedalling.

### Speed sessions
Don't confuse these anaerobic sessions with intervals. Speed sessions are for your absolute top speed. They have the added effect of targeting fast-twitch muscles, so muscle shape is improved, too. Speed sessions are full-on sprints

of 10 to 20 seconds, with periods between where you ride very easily for three to five minutes to ensure total recovery.

The science behind speed sessions is that sprinting is fuelled by the creatine phosphate system. A lot of energy is available for very powerful muscle contractions, but it is exhausted in a few seconds and requires at least three minutes to fully recharge.

Most cyclists need only one or two speed sessions a week, and they can be tagged onto another workout. Do three to five sprints with sufficient rest between them just after your warm up and before the rest of the session.

### Hill repetitions
You can use hills in a number of ways. Riding hills is the best way to improve your ability to cope with them in a race or similar challenge. But hills can also be used for raising your anaerobic threshold and building your capacity to ride really hard.

Long climbs in a gear that you can spin at 90 revs per minute, and ride at a pace that you can just about manage for 20 minutes, are a great way to raise your anaerobic threshold. Steep climbs lasting two to five minutes that make you climb in and out of the saddle are good capacity intervals.

To really test your muscles, especially your core, try riding uphill seated in the saddle in a gear that is higher than you would normally use. This is challenging because you have to resist the force throwing you from side to side.

# Pedal power

## Be strong in the saddle with this cycling-specific workout

**S**uccessful cycling is all about transmitting power efficiently from your body to the pedals. The main force drivers are your legs, but they need to be supported by a strong core. Time in the saddle will help condition your body for cycling, but spending time in the gym doing cycling-specific exercises will also give you a huge boost. And the benefits aren't limited to power-hungry pursuits such as intense sprints. One recent American study found that a 12-week resistance training programme increased cyclists' time to exhaustion by 33 per cent, meaning they could ride much further at a given intensity level. The following exercises mimic the movements you make when you're on a bike. They will help your muscles communicate with your brain so you get better at performing that kind of movement. Do them in order on non-cycling days, concentrating on the concentric (muscle-shortening) phase, and perform them explosively so you get used to moving at speed.

### 1 Dumb-bell step-up
**Sets:** 3 **Reps:** 12 each side

■ Look forward with your back upright and place your whole foot on the bench.
■ Push up with your leading leg.
■ Step back down with the trailing leg and repeat as before for all the reps before swapping sides.

**Why do it?** Generating power in one leg from a position where your knee is bent at 90° mimics the movement of pedalling.

### One-leg Romanian deadlift
**Sets:** 3 **Reps:** 12 each side

■ Grip the bar just outside your hips.
■ Stand on one leg, keep your shoulders back and your core engaged.
■ Initiate the move by leaning forward from the hips not the waist.
■ Keep your back flat and send the weight down your leg.

**Why do it?** This move promotes single-leg stability, which is vital in cycling, and prepares your muscles for the deadlift later in the workout.

### Squat with stretch band
**Sets:** 3 **Reps:** 12

■ Tie a stretch band just above your knees so you feel the tension.
■ Lower until your thighs are parallel to the floor.

**Why do it?** The stretch band forces you to keep your legs together, which encourages them to move in an efficient, piston-like way when you're on the bike.

### 4 Deadlift
**Sets:** 3 **Reps:** 12

■ Start with your feet shoulder-width apart, keeping your back flat, shoulders back and an overhand grip.
■ Start the move by pushing with your glutes, then push through your heels and lift the bar up your shins.

**Why do it?** This whole-body move gets you moving as one unit, working the kinetic chain that runs from your upper-back muscles down to your legs.

## 5 One-leg band press
**Sets:** 3 **Reps:** 12 each side

■ Lie on your back with one end of
a heavy-resistance stretchband in
each hand.
■ Bend your left knee and raise your left
foot up towards you so that you can loop
the band under your foot.
■ Press the leg away from you, keeping
your lower back flat on the floor.

**Why do it?** This move replicates the
downward stroke of the pedal revolution,
while the instability of the band teaches
you to control the movement.

## 6 Bicycles
**Sets:** 3 **Time:** 20-40 seconds

■ Crunch up and bring your left elbow
to your right knee.
■ Twist your torso from side to side while
pumping your legs back and forth.

**Why do it?** Your core can switch
off while you're riding, so this move
makes sure you're strong across your
abs and core.

# Cycle stabilisers

## Do this stability workout for more efficiency and fewer injuries

Functional movements such as the ones performed in sport require a high level of stability to control your body because it's not fixed into one plane of motion. When your legs move through a pedal revolution, you want them to exert force in a piston-like way, rather than losing power by deviating to the sides. To do

that, you need to be stable through the muscles, ligaments and tendons in your legs and through your core, hips and lower back.

Good core stability is vital because the forces generated by your legs must pass through those muscles. If you have a weak core, some of the force will be dissipated and lost. But while

core stability is important for cycling, you won't improve it dramatically by spending time in the saddle, because the riding position encourages those muscles to switch off. Do the following exercises in order, once or twice a week on non-cycling days to keep your core strong and help reduce your chances of injury.

---

## 1 Leg drop
**Sets** 3: **Reps:** 15 each side

■ Lie on your back with your legs straight and your arms stretched out for balance.
■ Lift your right leg straight up into the air and, keeping your shoulders in contact with the ground, bring it across your body, rotating your hips until your right foot is an inch above the floor.
■ Hold that position for one second and return to the start.
■ Repeat the move on the opposite leg and alternate for 15 reps on each leg.

**Why do it?** This exercise will promote flexibility in your hips, protecting you against injury.

## 2 One-leg bench squat
**Sets:** 3 **Reps:** 12 each side

■ Stand on a bench with one foot hanging over the edge.
■ Keep your back straight and your standing knee in line with your foot.
■ Lower your body as far as you can (or until your thigh is parallel with the floor) and return to the start.

**Why do it?** The unstable nature of this exercise means that you have to keep your knee in line with your foot, which encourages an efficient pedalling position.

## 3 Barbell roll-out
**Sets:** 3 **Reps:** 12

■ Grip the bar just wider than shoulder-width apart.
■ Keep your back straight and start with the barbell beneath your shoulders.
■ Roll the bar out as far as you can without overreaching.
■ Use your abdominals to control the movement, making it slow and deliberate.

**Why do it?** This move gets your core and lower back muscles working together to stabilise your body, which will protect you from injury on long rides.

## 4 Gym ball hip roller
**Sets:** 2 **Reps:** 15

■ Sit on a gym ball with your arms across your chest and your knees bent.
■ Brace your abs, lean back and tilt your hips by rolling them forward, pressing into the ball with your glutes.
■ Roll your hips back to bring your torso upright, keeping your shoulders back so you sit up straight.

**Why do it?** This exercise improves posture and core strength so you can cycle for longer and maintain speed.

## 5 Seated Russian twist with medicine ball
**Sets:** 3 **Reps:** 12 each side

■ Sit on a mat with your knees bent at 45° and your body held at 45° to the floor.
■ Keep your back straight, look forward and twist your torso to one side.
■ Stay looking forward, maintain the angle of your body to the floor and twist your torso to the other side.
■ Use your abs to control the momentum of the medicine ball.

**Why do it?** This rotational move works your obliques and core, which will keep you stable on the bike when you're climbing hills.

## 6 Gym ball plank
**Sets:** 3 **Time:** 20 seconds

■ Position your feet together on a bench with your elbows and forearms resting on a gym ball.
■ Keep your elbows beneath your shoulders and hold your body in a straight line from head to heels.
■ Don't let your hips drop below the horizontal.

**Why do it?** By building a strong link between your upper and lower body, this challenging move helps to improve your overall stability and posture.

# Cycle with care

Looking after your bike and making sure it's fit to pedal gives you a smoother ride and keeps it on the road for longer

## Keeping your bike clean

Not only does a clean bike look better, it works better and lasts longer, too. Road dirt and old lubricant act as a grinding paste, wearing out components fast. Plus, dirt hides stuff that might become a problem, such as cuts in tyres and chipped paint that could lead to corrosion. Here's how to look after your bike to minimise wear and tear.

■ You should clean your bike once a week and after every wet ride. If you don't have time to do the whole thing, just clean the drive train, which is the chain, chainset and sprockets.

■ Wash the frame with hot, soapy water, using sponges, cloths and different sized brushes to get into the hard-to-reach places. Start at the top of the frame and work down.

■ Remove the wheels and use degreaser and a stiff brush to clean the drive train. Wash off the degreaser with hot, soapy water. Dry, and lubricate with a bike-specific lubricant.

■ With a different stiff brush and more hot, soapy water, clean both wheels. Work the water in between the spokes and around the hubs. Scrub the tyres, and check for cuts.

■ Rinse the wheels and frame with clean water and dry them with a clean cloth. Reassemble and check the frame for blemishes and wear.

Clean the chain, chainset and sprockets

Wash the frame with hot, soapy water

Remove both wheels

Wash the wheels with hot, soapy water and check the tyres for cuts

# Pre-ride checks

These checks don't take long, but are essential for safety. Get into the habit of doing them before each ride. Also, have a close look at the frame once a week. Use touch-up paint to cover any chips. If you discover a crack, return the bike to where you bought it.

■ Apply each brake fully while trying to push your bike forward. Neither wheel should turn. Adjust the brake blocks so they contact the wheel squarely if they do not do so when the brake is applied. Also, check the brake blocks for wear and replace them if there is any. Inspect the cables inside brake levers for fraying and replace them if you see any. Hold the front wheel between your legs and try to turn the handlebars. They shouldn't move.

■ Lift the front of the bike and slowly turn the front wheel, inspecting the tyres for bulges, cuts or excessive wear. Repeat for the back wheel and replace the tyre if you see any defects. If either wheel touches the brake blocks when the brakes aren't applied, the wheel isn't running true or the brakes need attention. A good bike shop will advise you on how to fix the problem.

■ Check that the quick-release levers on your wheels are in the locked position. Most have the words lock and unlock written on them. Lock should be outermost. If yours don't have those words on them, get familiar with how they work and how they look when locked. Check that the bottle cages, bags, pump and saddle are secure.

■ Gear shifts that aren't perfect can distract you when riding, and having your chain slip out of gear can cause injury. With the rear wheel raised, run through all the gear shifts. If shifts aren't instant and smooth, or there is chain noise when running on a particular sprocket of chainring, the rear or front mech needs adjusting. If you bought your bike new, instructions for this should come with it.

Apply both brakes fully while trying to push the bike forwards

Turn the front wheel and inspect the tyre

Check the quick-release levers

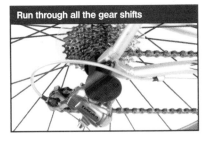

Run through all the gear shifts

# Repairing a puncture

**1** You need a puncture repair kit containing glue, patches, a crayon marker, French chalk and some kind of abrasive material. You also need at least two tyre levers.

**2** Remove the wheel, then insert the blunt end of a tyre lever between the tyre and wheel rim. Lever the edge of the tyre over the rim. With the lever still inserted, hook the other end around a spoke. Insert the second lever and push this around the tyre to lift it off, then remove the inner tube.

**3** Lift the tyre completely off the wheel and inspect it inside and out for cuts and anything sticking into it. A deeply cut tyre needs replacing. Remove any objects stuck in the tyre by pulling them out from the outside.

**4** Inflate the inner tube and listen for escaping air to locate the hole. Mark it, then work around the whole tube listening out for more holes. Deflate the tube and roughen the surface around any holes with abrasive material. Select a repair patch and spread a thin layer of glue over the roughened area, which should be slightly larger than the repair patch.

**5** Allow the glue to go tacky then peel the backing from the patch and firmly press it, backside down, onto the glue. Ensure that the patch edges are flat and keep pressure on it for about a minute. Use the abrasive material to dust some French chalk onto the repair. Allow the glue to dry fully.

**6** Put one side of the tyre fully onto the rim. Inflate the tube slightly and push its valve down through the rim hole. Work the whole of the tube onto the rim and under the tyre. Push the valve upwards slightly and lift the other side of the tyre over the rim. Work the rest of the tyre back onto the rim. If it proves difficult use a tyre lever to help fit the last part. Inflate the tube fully.

Insert the blunt end of a tyre lever between the tyre and the wheel rim

Inspect the tyre inside and out for cuts and anything sticking through it

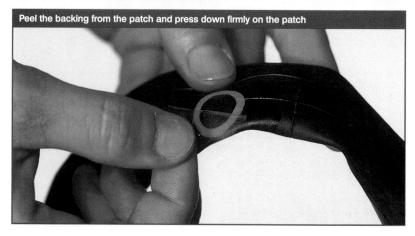
Peel the backing from the patch and press down firmly on the patch

# Workshop briefing

Follow this advice on how to minimise bike damage and fix common problems

**Q** How often should I get my bike serviced?

**A** Get it fully serviced twice a year, once before the winter and again before the summer. You should also do a weekly degrease, clean and lubrication of the drive train.

**Q** How do I make my rear gear shifts smoother?

**A** Undo the bolt securing the cable to the rear mech. Adjust the H screw so the chain runs smoothly on the smallest sprocket. Re-attach the cable and shift through the gears. If any shifts are slow or the chain doesn't sit well on the sprocket, use the cable adjuster, located where the cable enters the rear mech, turning it one way or the other until the problem is solved.

**Q** How do I prolong the life of the bearings on my bike?

**A** Check cranks, pedals, hubs and headset for looseness or over tightness. If you find any, adjust it yourself using the instructions in a good bike maintenance book, or take the bike to a good bike shop.

**Q** How do I cut down wear to the drive train?

**A** Replace any worn individual part before it wears out the rest. For example, a worn chain will quickly wear out sprockets and chainrings. Chains should be replaced every six months. If your chain jumps on a single sprocket, that sprocket could be worn and should be replaced.

**Q** How do I prevent my brakes screeching or juddering?

**A** Inspect the brake blocks and remove with tweezers any foreign bodies that might become embedded in them. This cuts down on rim wear,

too. Clean wheel rims with solvent to remove any residue that could affect brake performance.

**Q** How can I increase the life of my tyres?

**A** Always inflate them to a pressure in accordance with the manufacturer's instructions, which are usually printed on the tyre wall. Brush off anything that might be stuck to them after each ride before it gets embedded in the tyre.

**Q** How can I protect my frame from scratches?

**A** If it hasn't got one, fit a chain-stay protector on the side where the chain runs. This will stop it chipping the paintwork when riding over rough surfaces. Protect places where the various cables rub against the frame with special patches that fit between the cables and frame.

# Quicker, smarter

## Get ahead of the pack with these performance boosting hints

### Pedal in circles

Correct pedalling technique circulates power through as much of the pedal revolution as possible. Push each pedal forward at the top of each revolution and pull it back at the bottom, rather like scraping something off the sole of your shoe. Relax, or even pull up with, the ascending leg as well as pushing down with the descending one.

### Use visualisation for training inspiration

Add spark to an interval session by copying how the pros attack. When doing an interval, pretend you are in a race and go hard, imagining you are covering an attack, then go harder when you catch your rival to attack him. Or make an even bigger effort over the top of a hill after going hard up it. That's how the pros break up a race.

### Go long for endurance

Pick a day that you can devote to cycling, then look at the weather forecast. Book you and your bike onto a train going to a place as much as 100 miles away, and where the wind is behind you on the ride back. You will get a long ride that's not too taxing, but still gives your endurance a huge boost. Plus, your mates will be amazed by the distance you've covered.

### Smooth riding

When riding, make all your actions (braking, shifting gears, getting out of the saddle and sitting back down again) as smooth as possible. Keep pedalling when you shift gear, but ease the pressure slightly at the moment the chain is in transit, especially when shifting between chainrings. Do this and you'll even be able to make smooth shifts when riding out of the saddle.

## Pace-line training for speed

You need two or three other riders for this. After a warm up, one rider sets the pace and the others follow in the slipstream. After 30 seconds the front rider moves out and drops to the back of the pace-line, while the next rider sets the pace, and so on. Do bursts of five minutes sharing the pace-line lead, all riding as hard as you can.

## Spread your effort on hills

Don't hammer up a hill from the start. Hold back a bit and build your effort as you climb, saving some strength to pick up speed over the top. Consider the top of the hill to be the first few metres of the descent, and make your effort last until then. You slow down rapidly if you ease off or are exhuasted by the top.

## Take your road bike off road to improve skills

You don't need mountain bike country for this, just a bit of wood or parkland. Make sure you have right of way on your bike. Cornering, climbing and descending on loose surfaces or wet grass improves your bike skills by increasing your sensitivity to what is going on under your wheels.

## Use numbers for motivation

Cycling lends itself to numbers, so record everything you can think of. Get a bike computer to record distances and times of rides, plus as much other information as possible. Weigh yourself regularly. Record body measurements. Something, somewhere will be improving, and there is nothing like seeing improvement for keeping you motivated.

## Ride with rhythm

The best bike racers can get into a groove and bash out a furious pedalling rhythm without tiring. It's like they have some sort of beat going in their heads. Actually, that's not too far out. Top pros try to synchronise their pedalling and breathing. Music can help, too. Not necessarily from an iPod, but a powerful, motivational tune that you can keep in your head and use the tempo for inspiration whenever you need it.

**Use a circuit to improve cornering**

Find some relatively traffic-free roads that make up a circuit. Make sure there are three or four sharp corners in it. If traffic allows, move out before each corner and move in across the apex to take as much speed through the corner as possible. Accelerate hard out of each corner, then ride easy before accelerating for the next. After a couple of laps, turn around and do take corners from the opposite direction.

# Plan of action

## Use these goal-specific plans to turn training into high performance

Following a structured training plan is the most effective way to improve your fitness. A plan maps out your progress, placing each session where it is needed to bring about improvements. That gives you the right mix of training overload and rest your body needs to make the adaptations that result in improved fitness.

The following plans are designed for specific cycling challenges. The first will give a newcomer a base level of cycling fitness. The second is for someone with some cycling experience who wants to take part in a 50-mile cyclosportive event and the third is for anyone fancying a crack at a longer cyclosportive event, such as the Étape du Tour, a stage of the Tour de France open to all comers.

The final plan is for a time-trial event. It will raise your anaerobic threshold and your capacity to ride hard over a short period.

# Beginners plan

## Get on your bike and get fit fast with this three-month plan

This plan gets your muscles used to cycling. It revolves around riding at a steady conversational pace for increasing lengths of time and it will take you to a point where you can start training for some cycling events. The plan also contains some speed work to put a bit of zip into your riding and some higher-intensity training over longer periods of time to raise your anaerobic threshold. You will need a variety of routes, including flat, rolling and hilly rides, plus a circuit of three miles to do a monthly progress-assessing time trial.

### ■ Week 1

**Monday**
Ride at level 5 for 40 mins on a flat route

**Tuesday**
Rest

**Wednesday**
Level 5 for 40 mins on a flat route (2x15 secs sprints mid ride)

**Thursday**
Rest

**Friday**
Level 5 for 40 mins, rolling route

**Saturday**
Rest

**Sunday**
Level 5 for 60 mins

### ■ Week 2

**Monday**
Rest

**Tuesday**
Level 5 for 45 mins on a flat route

**Wednesday**
Rest

**Thursday**
Level 5 for 45 mins, rolling route

**Friday**
Rest

**Saturday**
Level 4 on a flat route for 40 mins (3x15 secs sprints mid ride)

**Sunday**
Level 5 for 70 mins

### ■ Week 3

**Monday**
Rest

**Tuesday**
Level 5 for 50 mins on a flat route

**Wednesday**
Rest

**Thursday**
Level 5 for 50 mins, rolling route

**Friday**
Rest

**Saturday**
Level 4 on a flat route for 40 mins (3x30 secs seated fast pedals mid ride)

**Sunday**
Level 5 for 80 mins

### ■ Week 4

**Monday**
Level 4 for 40 mins on a flat route

**Tuesday**
Rest

**Wednesday**
Level 5 for 40 mins on a flat route

**Thursday**
Rest

**Friday**
Level 4 for 10 mins (ride a time trial on test circuit). Level 4 for 10 mins

**Saturday**
Rest

**Sunday**
Rest

### ■ Week 5

**Monday**
Level 5 for 50 mins on rolling route, level 6 uphill

**Tuesday**
Rest

**Wednesday**
As Monday

**Thursday**
Rest

**Friday**
Level 5 for 50 mins, flat route (4x30 secs seated fast pedals mid ride)

**Saturday**
Rest

**Sunday**
Level 5 for 70 mins

### ■ Week 6

**Monday**
Rest

**Tuesday**
Level 5 for 50 mins on a hilly route, level 6 uphill

**Wednesday**
Rest

**Thursday**
As Tuesday

**Friday**
Rest

**Saturday**
Level 4 for 40 mins (3x15 secs sprints mid ride)

**Sunday**
Level 5 for 80 mins

### ■ Week 7

**Monday**
Rest

**Tuesday**
Level 5 for 60mins on rolling route, level 6-7 uphill

**Wednesday**
Rest

**Thursday**
As Tuesday

**Friday**
Rest

**Saturday**
Level 4 for 40 mins on a flat route (3x30 secs seated fast pedals mid ride)

**Sunday**
Level 5 for 80 mins

### ■ Week 8

**Monday**
Level 4 for 40 mins on a flat route

**Tuesday**
Rest

**Wednesday**
Level 5 for 40 mins on a flat route

**Thursday**
Rest

**Friday**
Level 4-5 for 10 mins, time trial on test circuit, level 4 for 10 mins

**Saturday**
Rest

**Sunday**
Rest

### ■ Week 9

**Monday**
Level 5 on flat route for 60 mins (middle 15 mins at level 6-7)

**Tuesday**
Rest

**Wednesday**
As Monday

**Thursday**
Rest

**Friday**
Level for 60 mins on flat route (4x30 secs fast pedals mid ride)

**Saturday**
Rest

**Sunday**
Level 5 for 90 mins

### ■ Week 10

**Monday**
Rest

**Tuesday**
Level 5 on flat route for 60 mins (middle 20 mins at level 6-7 in a gear just higher than comfortable)

**Wednesday**
Rest

**Thursday**
As Tuesday

**Friday**
Rest

**Saturday**
Rest

**Sunday**
Level 4 for 40 mins

### ■ Week 11

**Monday**
Rest

**Tuesday**
Level 5 for 60 mins on hilly route, level 6-7 uphill in a higher than normal gear

**Wednesday**
Rest

**Thursday**
As Tuesday

**Friday**
Rest

**Saturday**
Level 4 for 40 mins (3x30 secs seated fast pedals mid ride)

**Sunday**
Level 5 for 100 mins

### ■ Week 12

**Monday**
Level 5 for 40 mins on a flat route

**Tuesday**
Rest

**Wednesday**
As Monday

**Thursday**
Rest

**Friday**
Level 4-5 for 10 mins, time trial on test circuit, level 4 for 10 mins

**Saturday**
Rest

**Sunday**
Level 4 for 40 mins on a flat route

# 50 mile cyclosportive plan weeks 1-16

## Get ready to take on serious riders with this six-month plan

This plan is for anyone who has done a fair bit of cycling and wants to have a go at a 50-mile cyclosportive event. You tend not to find 50-mile courses in mountainous regions, so this plan focuses on the endurance required to ride hard for around three hours, and builds the fitness and strength to cope with lots of short, sharp hills. It's perfect for an event in Britain or northern Europe. You'll need a range of routes (flat, rolling and hilly), a steepish hill for repeats and a time-trial test course of around three miles. Record your time round this circuit once a month.

| ■ Week 1 | ■ Week 2 | ■ Week 3 | ■ Week 4 | ■ Week 5 | ■ Week 6 | ■ Week 7 | ■ Week 8 |
|---|---|---|---|---|---|---|---|
| **Monday** Rest or ride at level 4 for 40 mins on a flat route | **Monday** Rest | **Monday** Rest | **Monday** Level 4 for 40 mins on a flat route | **Monday** Level 5 for 60 mins on a flat route | **Monday** Rest | **Monday** Rest | **Monday** Level 4 for 40 mins on a flat route |
| **Tuesday** Rest | **Tuesday** Level 5-6 for 60 mins on a rolling route, level 7 uphill | **Tuesday** Level 5-6 for 70 mins on a rolling route, level 7 uphill | **Tuesday** Rest | **Tuesday** Rest | **Tuesday** Level 5-6 for 60 mins on a hilly route (pushing almost to level 8 uphill) | **Tuesday** Level 5-6 for 60 mins (20 mins at level 7 mid ride) | **Tuesday** Rest |
| **Wednesday** Level 5-6 for 60 mins on a rolling route, level 7 uphill | **Wednesday** Rest | **Wednesday** Rest | **Wednesday** Level 5-6 for 60 mins on a flat route | **Wednesday** Level 5-6 for 75 mins on a rolling route, level 7 uphill | **Wednesday** Rest | **Wednesday** Rest | **Wednesday** Level 5-6 for 60 mins on a flat route |
| **Thursday** Rest | **Thursday** Level 5-6 for 60 mins on a flat route (15 mins at level 7 mid ride) | **Thursday** Level 5-6 for 60 mins on a flat route (2x10 mins at level 7 mid ride, with 5 mins level 4 between) | **Thursday** Rest | **Thursday** Rest | **Thursday** Level 5-6 for 75 mins on a rolling route | **Thursday** Level 5-6 for 60 mins on a hilly route (2x3 mins hill repeats at level 7-8 mid ride with 3 mins level 4 between) | **Thursday** Rest |
| **Friday** Level 5-6 for 75 mins on a flat route (15 mins at level 7 mid ride) | **Friday** Rest | **Friday** Rest | **Friday** Level 4 into 5-6 for 10 mins, time trial on test circuit, level 4 for 10 mins | **Friday** Level 5-6 for 60 mins on a hilly route, level 7 uphill | **Friday** Rest | **Friday** Rest | **Friday** Level 4 into 5-6 for 10 mins, ride, time trial on test circuit, level 4 for 10 mins |
| **Saturday** Rest | **Saturday** Level 4 for 40 mins on a flat route (3x15 secs sprints mid ride, with 5 mins at level 4 between) | **Saturday** Level 5-6 for 60 mins on a flat route | **Saturday** Rest | **Saturday** Rest | **Saturday** Level 5-6 for 60 mins on Brick session: bike 8km, run 4km without resting a flat route | **Saturday** Level 4 for 40 mins on a flat route (3x15 secs sprints mid ride with 5 mins at level 4 between) | **Saturday** Rest |
| **Sunday** Level 5 for 90 mins on a flat route | **Sunday** Level 5 for 105 mins on a flat route | **Sunday** Level 5 for 120 mins on a flat route | **Sunday** Level 5 for 120 mins on a flat route | **Sunday** Level 5-6 for 90 mins on a flat route. | **Sunday** Level 5-6 for 105 mins on a flat route | **Sunday** Level 5-6 for 120 mins on a flat route | **Sunday** Level 5 for 120 mins on a flat route |

| ■ Week 9 | ■ Week 10 | ■ Week 11 | ■ Week 12 | ■ Week 13 | ■ Week 14 | ■ Week 15 | ■ Week 16 |
|---|---|---|---|---|---|---|---|
| **Monday**<br>Level 5 for 60 mins on a flat route | **Monday**<br>Rest | **Monday**<br>Rest | **Monday**<br>Level 4 for 40 mins on a flat route (3x15 secs sprints mid ride, with 5 mins at level 4 between) | **Monday**<br>Level 5 for 60 mins on a flat route | **Monday**<br>Rest | **Monday**<br>Rest | **Monday**<br>Level 5 for 60 mins on a flat route |
| **Tuesday**<br>Rest | **Tuesday**<br>Level 5-6 for 60 mins on a hilly route, pushing to level 9 uphill | **Tuesday**<br>Level 5-6 for 60 mins on a hilly route (4x3 mins hill repeats at level 7-8 mid ride, with 3 mins at level 4 between) | **Tuesday**<br>Rest | **Tuesday**<br>Rest | **Tuesday**<br>Level 5-6 for 60 mins on a hilly route (3x5 mins hill repeats at level 7-8 mid ride, with 3 mins at level 4 between) | **Tuesday**<br>Level 5-6 for 60 mins (2x15 mins at level 6-7 mid ride in a slightly higher gear than feels comfortable, with 5 mins at level 4 between) | **Tuesday**<br>Rest |
| **Wednesday**<br>Level 5-6 for 60 mins on a rolling route (20 mins at level 7 mid ride) | **Wednesday**<br>Rest | **Wednesday**<br>Rest | **Wednesday**<br>Level 5-6 for 60 mins on a flat route | **Wednesday**<br>Level 5-6 for 60 mins (2x15 mins at level 6-7 mid ride, with 5 mins at level 4 between) | **Wednesday**<br>Rest | **Wednesday**<br>Rest | **Wednesday**<br>Level 5-6 for 60 mins on a flat route |
| **Thursday**<br>Rest | **Thursday**<br>Level 5-6 for 60 mins (20 mins at level 7 mid ride) | **Thursday**<br>Level 5-6 for 60 mins (20 mins at level 7 mid ride) | **Thursday**<br>Rest | **Thursday**<br>Rest | **Thursday**<br>Level 5-6 for 60 mins on a hilly route (5x1 mins hill repeats at level 8-9 mid ride, with 3 mins at level 4 between) | **Thursday**<br>Level 5-6 for 75 mins on a hilly route (5x1 min hill repeats at level 8-9 mid ride, with 3 mins at level 4 between) | **Thursday**<br>Rest |
| **Friday**<br>Level 5-6 for 60 mins on a hilly route (3x3 mins hill repeats at level 7-8 mid ride, with 3 mins at level 4 between) | **Friday**<br>Rest | **Friday**<br>Rest | **Friday**<br>Level 4 into 5-6 for 10 mins, time trial on test circuit, level 4 for 10 mins | **Friday**<br>Level 5-6 for 60 mins on a hilly route (5x1 mins hill repeats at level 8-9 mid ride, with 3 mins at level 4 between) | **Friday**<br>Rest | **Friday**<br>Rest | **Friday**<br>Level 4 into 5-6 for 10 mins, time trial on test circuit, level 4 for 10 mins |
| **Saturday**<br>Rest | **Saturday**<br>Level 4 for 60 mins (4x1 mins hill repeats at level 8-9 mid ride, with 3 mins at level 4 between) | **Saturday**<br>Level 4 for 40 mins on a flat route (3x15 secs sprints mid ride, with 5 mins at level 4 between) | **Saturday**<br>Rest | **Saturday**<br>Rest | **Saturday**<br>Level 4 for 40 mins on a flat route (3x15 secs sprints mid ride, with 5 mins at level 4 between) | **Saturday**<br>Level 4 for 40 mins on a flat route (3x15 secs sprints mid ride, with 5 mins at level 4 between) | **Saturday**<br>Rest |
| **Sunday**<br>Level 5-6 for 150 mins on a flat route | **Sunday**<br>Level 5-6 for 170 mins on a flat route | **Sunday**<br>Level 5-6 for 180 mins on a flat route | **Sunday**<br>Level 5 for 120 mins on a flat route | **Sunday**<br>Level 5-6 for 120 mins on a rolling route, level 7 uphill | **Sunday**<br>Level 5-6 for 150 mins on a rolling route, level 7 uphill | **Sunday**<br>Level 5-6 for 180 mins on a rolling route, level 7 uphill | **Sunday**<br>Level 5 for 120 mins on a flat route |

# 50 mile cyclosportive plan weeks 17-24

| Week 17 | Week 18 | Week 19 | Week 20 | Week 21 | Week 22 | Week 23 | Week 24 |
|---|---|---|---|---|---|---|---|
| **Monday** Level 5 for 60 mins on a flat route | **Monday** Rest | **Monday** Rest | **Monday** Level 5 for 60 mins on a flat route | **Monday** Level 5 for 60 mins on a flat route | **Monday** Rest | **Monday** Rest | **Monday** Level 5 for 60 mins on a flat route |
| **Tuesday** Rest | **Tuesday** Level 5-6 for 60 mins on a hilly route (4x5 mins level 7-8 hill repeats mid ride, with 3 mins at level 4 between) | **Tuesday** Level 5-6 for 60 mins (2x15 mins at level 6-7 mid ride in a slightly higher gear than feels comfortable, with 5 mins at level 4 between) | **Tuesday** Rest | **Tuesday** Rest | **Tuesday** Level 5-6 for 60 mins (2x15 mins at level 6-7 mid ride, with 5 mins at level 4 between) | **Tuesday** Level 5-6 for 60 mins (2x15 mins at level 6-7 mid ride, with 5 mins at level 4 between | **Tuesday** Rest |
| **Wednesday** Level 5-6 for 75 mins on a hilly route (5x1 mins hill repeats at level 8-9 mid ride, with 3 mins at level 4 between) | **Wednesday** Rest | **Wednesday** Rest | **Wednesday** Level 5-6 for 60 mins on a flat route | **Wednesday** Level 5-6 for 75 mins on a hilly route (5x1 mins level 8-9 hill repeats mid ride, with 3 mins at level 4 between) | **Wednesday** Rest | **Wednesday** Rest | **Wednesday** Level 5-6 for 60 mins on a flat route |
| **Thursday** Rest | **Thursday** Level 5-6 for 60 mins on a hilly route (5x1 mins level 8-9 hill repeats mid ride, with 3 mins at level 4 between) | **Thursday** Level 5-6 for 60 mins (2x15 mins at level 6-7 mid ride in a slightly higher gear than feels comfortable, with 5 mins at level 4 between) | **Thursday** Rest | **Thursday** Rest | **Thursday** Level 5-6 for 60 mins on a hilly route (3x3 mins level 7-8 hill repeats mid ride, with 3 mins at level 4 between) | **Thursday** Level 5-6 for 60 mins on a hilly route (3x1 mins level 8-9 hill repeats mid ride, with 3 mins at level 4 between) | **Thursday** Rest |
| **Friday** Level 5-6 for 80 mins on a rolling route, level 6-7 uphill in a gear slightly higher than feels comfortable | **Friday** Rest | **Friday** Rest | **Friday** Level 4 into 5-6 for 10 mins, time trial on test circuit, level 4 for 10 mins | **Friday** Level 5-6 for 80 mins on a rolling route, level 6-7 uphill in a gear slightly higher than feels comfortable | **Friday** Rest | **Friday** Rest | **Friday** Level 4 into 5-6 for 10 mins, time trial on test circuit, level 4 for 10 mins |
| **Saturday** Rest | **Saturday** Level 4 for 40 mins on a flat route (3x15 secs sprints mid ride, with 5 mins at level 4 between) | **Saturday** Level 4 for 40 mins on a flat route (3x15 secs sprints mid ride, with 5 mins at level 4 between) | **Saturday** Rest | **Saturday** Rest | **Saturday** Level 4 for 40 mins on a flat route (3x15 secs sprints mid ride, with 5 mins at level 4 between) | **Saturday** Level 4 for 40 mins on a flat route (3x15 secs sprints mid ride, with 5 mins at level 4 between) | **Saturday** Rest |
| **Sunday** Level 5-6 for 120 mins on a hilly route, level 7 uphill | **Sunday** Level 5-6 for 150 mins on a hilly route, level 7 uphill | **Sunday** Level 5-6 for 180 mins on a hilly route, level 7 uphill | **Sunday** Level 5 for 120 mins on a flat route | **Sunday** Level 5-6 for 150 mins on a hilly route, level 7 uphill | **Sunday** Level 5-6 for 180 mins on a hilly route, level 7 uphill | **Sunday** Level 5-6 for 120 mins on a rolling route, level 7 uphill | **Sunday** Level 5 for 120 mins on a flat route |

# 100-mile cyclosportive plan weeks 1-8

## Go long with this six-month 100-mile cyclosportive plan

This plan is aimed at riders who want to take part in long-distance cyclosportives, such as the Étape du Tour in France or the longer British events such as the Etape Caledonia in Scotland. You need a variety of routes (flat, rolling and hilly), plus the longest hill you can find for repeats, and a time-trial course of around three miles. Record your time on this circuit once a month. One key session is riding in a higher than normal gear, which simulates European mountain climbs. If you live in a flat area, do this by riding into the wind on the flat.

| ■ Week 1 | ■ Week 2 | ■ Week 3 | ■ Week 4 | ■ Week 5 | ■ Week 6 | ■ Week 7 | ■ Week 8 |
|---|---|---|---|---|---|---|---|
| **Monday** Ride at level 5-6 for 60 mins on a flat route | **Monday** Rest | **Monday** Rest | **Monday** Level 4 for 40 mins on a flat route | **Monday** Level 5 for 60 mins on a flat route | **Monday** Rest | **Monday** Rest | **Monday** Level 4 for 40 mins on a flat route |
| **Tuesday** Rest | **Tuesday** Level 5-6 for 75 mins on a rolling route, level 7 uphill | **Tuesday** Level 5-6 for 70 mins on a rolling route, level 7 uphill using a gear slightly higher than comfortable | **Tuesday** Rest | **Tuesday** Level 5-6 for 60 mins on a rolling route, level 7 uphill | **Tuesday** Level 5-6 for 60 mins on a route with long hills (pushing to level 8 by top of each hill) | **Tuesday** Level 5-6 for 60 mins (20 mins level 7 mid ride in a gear slightly higher than comfortable) | **Tuesday** Rest |
| **Wednesday** Level 5-6 for 75 mins on a rolling route, level 7 uphill | **Wednesday** Rest | **Wednesday** Rest | **Wednesday** Level 5-6 for 60 mins on a flat route | **Wednesday** Level 5-6 for 75 mins on a rolling route, level 7 uphill using a gear slightly higher than comfortable | **Wednesday** Rest | **Wednesday** Rest | **Wednesday** Level 5-6 for 60 mins on a flat route |
| **Thursday** Rest | **Thursday** Level 5-6 for 60 mins on a rolling route (20 mins at level 7 mid ride) | **Thursday** Level 5-6 for 60 mins on a flat route (2x10 mins level 7 mid ride in gear slightly higher than comfortable, with 5 mins at level 4 between) | **Thursday** Rest | **Thursday** Rest | **Thursday** Level 5-6 for 75 mins on a rolling route, level 7 uphill using a gear slightly higher than comfortable | **Thursday** Level 5-6 for 60 mins on a hilly route (2x7-10 mins level 7 hill repeats mid ride, with 5 mins at level 4 between) | **Thursday** Rest |
| **Friday** Level 5-6 for 75 mins on a flat route (15 mins at level 7 mid ride) | **Friday** Rest | **Friday** Rest | **Friday** Level 4 into 5-6 for 10 mins, time trial on test circuit, level 4 for 10 mins | **Friday** Level 5-6 for 60 mins on a hilly route, level 7 uphill | **Friday** Rest | **Friday** Rest | **Friday** Level 4 into 5-6 for 10 mins, time trial on test circuit, level 4 for 10 mins |
| **Saturday** Rest | **Saturday** Level 4 for 40 mins on a flat route (3x15 secs sprints mid ride, with 5 mins at level 4 between) | **Saturday** Level 5-6 for 60 mins on a flat route | **Saturday** Rest | **Saturday** Rest | **Saturday** Level 5-6 for 60 mins on a flat route | **Saturday** Level 4 for 40 mins (3x15 secs sprints mid ride, with 5 mins at level 4 between) | **Saturday** Rest |
| **Sunday** Level 5-6 for 120 mins on a flat route | **Sunday** Rest | **Sunday** Level 5-6 for 180 mins | **Sunday** Level 5-6 for 120 mins on a flat route | **Sunday** Level 5-6 for 150 mins on a flat route | **Sunday** Level 5-6 for 180 mins on a flat route | **Sunday** Level 5-6 for 200 mins | **Sunday** Level 5 for 120 mins on a flat route |

# 100-mile cyclosportive plan weeks 9-24

| ■ Week 9 | ■ Week 10 | ■ Week 11 | ■ Week 12 | ■ Week 13 | ■ Week 14 | ■ Week 15 | ■ Week 16 |
|---|---|---|---|---|---|---|---|
| **Monday** Level 5-6 for 60 mins on a flat route | **Monday** Rest | **Monday** Rest | **Monday** Level 4 for 40 mins on a flat route (3x15 secs sprints mid ride, with 5 mins at level 4 between) | **Monday** Level 5 for 60 mins on a flat route | **Monday** Rest | **Monday** Rest | **Monday** Level 5 for 60 mins on a flat route |
| **Tuesday** Level 5-6 for 60 mins on a rolling route, level 7 uphill | **Tuesday** Level 5-6 for 60 mins on a hilly route, level 9 uphill | **Tuesday** Level 5-6 for 90 mins on a hilly route (4x7-10 mins level 7-8 hill repeats mid ride, with 5 mins at level 4 between) | **Tuesday** Rest | **Tuesday** Level 5-6 for 60 mins on a rolling route, level 7 uphill | **Tuesday** Level 5-6 for 90 mins on a hilly route (4x7-10 mins hill repeats level 7 mid ride in a gear slightly higher than comfortable, with 5 mins at level 4 in between) | **Tuesday** Level 5-6 for 75 mins (2x15 mins level 6-7 in a slightly higher gear than feels comfortable, with 5 mins at level 4 between) | **Tuesday** Rest |
| **Wednesday** Level 5-6 for 60 mins on a rolling route (20 mins level 7 mid ride in a gear slightly higher than comfortable) | **Wednesday** Rest | **Wednesday** Rest | **Wednesday** Level 5-6 for 60 mins on a flat route | **Wednesday** Level 5-6 for 60 mins (2x15 mins level 6-7 mid ride, with 5 mins at level 4 between) | **Wednesday** Rest | **Wednesday** Rest | **Wednesday** Level 5-6 for 60 mins on a flat route |
| **Thursday** Rest | **Thursday** Level 5-6 for 60 mins (20 mins mid ride at level 7) | **Thursday** Level 5-6 for 60 mins (20 mins at level 7 mid ride in a gear slightly higher than feels comfortable | **Thursday** Rest | **Thursday** Rest | **Thursday** Level 5-6 for 60 mins on a hilly route (5x1 mins level 8-9 hill repeats mid ride, with 3 mins at level 4 between) | **Thursday** Level 5-6 for 75 mins on a hilly route (5x1 mins level 8-9 hill repeats mid ride, with 3 mins at level 4 between) | **Thursday** Rest |
| **Friday** Level 5-6 for 75 mins on a hilly route (3x7-10 mins level 7 hill repeats mid ride, with 5 mins at level 4 between) | **Friday** Rest | **Friday** Rest | **Friday** Level 4 into 5-6 for 10 mins, time trial on test circuit, level 4 for 10 mins | **Friday** Level 5-6 for 60 mins on a hilly route (5x1 mins level 8-9 hill repeats mid ride, with 3 mins at level 4 between) | **Friday** Rest | **Friday** Rest | **Friday** Level 4 into 5-6 for 10 mins, time trial on test circuit, level 4 for 10 mins |
| **Saturday** Level 5-6 for 60 mins on a flat route | **Saturday** Level 4 for 60 mins (4x1 mins level 8-9 hill repeats mid ride, with 3 mins at level 4 between) | **Saturday** Level 4 for 40 mins on a flat route (3x15 secs sprints mid ride, with 5 mins at level 4 between) | **Saturday** Rest | **Saturday** Rest | **Saturday** Level 4 for 40 mins on a flat route (3x15 secs sprints mid ride, with 5 mins at level 4 between) | **Saturday** Level 4 for 40 mins on a flat route (3x15 secs sprints mid ride, with 5 mins at level 4 between) | **Saturday** Rest |
| **Sunday** Level 5-6 for 200 mins on a flat route | **Sunday** Level 5-6 for 220 mins on a flat route | **Sunday** Level 5-6 for 240 mins on a flat route | **Sunday** Level 5 for 120 mins on a flat route | **Sunday** Level 5-6 for 150 mins on a rolling route, level 7 uphill | **Sunday** Level 5-6 for 180 mins on a rolling route, level 7 uphill | **Sunday** Level 5-6 for 200 mins on a rolling route, level 7 uphill | **Sunday** Level 5 for 120 mins on a flat route |

| ■ Week 17 | ■ Week 18 | ■ Week 19 | ■ Week 20 | ■ Week 21 | ■ Week 22 | ■ Week 23 | ■ Week 24 |
|---|---|---|---|---|---|---|---|
| **Monday** Level 5 for 60 mins on a flat route | **Monday** Rest | **Monday** Rest | **Monday** Level 5 for 60 mins on a flat route | **Monday** Level 5 for 60 mins on a flat route | **Monday** Rest | **Monday** Rest | **Monday** Level 5 for 60 mins on a flat route |
| **Tuesday** Level 5-6 for 60 mins on a rolling route, level 7 uphill | **Tuesday** Level 5-6 for 90 mins on a hilly route (4x7-10 mins level 7 hill repeats mid ride, with 3 mins level 4 between) | **Tuesday** Level 5-6 for 60 mins (2x15 mins level 6-7 in a slightly higher gear than feels comfortable mid ride, with 5 mins level 4 between) | **Tuesday** Rest | **Tuesday** Level 5-6 for 60 mins on a rolling route, level 7 uphill | **Tuesday** Level 5-6 for 75 mins (2x15 mins level 6-7 in a gear slightly higher than comfortable mid ride, with 5 mins level 4 between) | **Tuesday** Level 5-6 for 60 mins (2x15 mins level 6-7 mid ride, with 5 mins level 4 between) | **Tuesday** Rest |
| **Wednesday** Level 5-6 for 75 mins on a hilly route (5x1 mins level 8-9 hill repeats mid ride, with 3 mins level 4 between) | **Wednesday** Rest | **Wednesday** Rest | **Wednesday** Level 5-6 for 60 mins on a flat route | **Wednesday** Level 5-6 for 75 mins on a hilly route (5x1 mins level 8-9 hill repeats mid ride, with 3 mins level 4 between) | **Wednesday** Rest | **Wednesday** Rest | **Wednesday** Level 5-6 for 60 mins on a flat route |
| **Thursday** Rest | **Thursday** Level 5-6 for 60 mins on a hilly route (5x1 mins level 8-9 hill repeats mid ride, with 3 mins level 4 between) | **Thursday** Level 5-6 for 60 mins on a hilly route (5x3 mins level 7-8 hill repeats mid ride, with 3 mins level 4 between) | **Thursday** Rest | **Thursday** Rest | **Thursday** Level 5-6 for 75 mins on a hilly route (3x5 mins level 7-8 hill repeats mid ride, with 3 mins level 4 between) | **Thursday** Level 5-6 for 60 mins on a hilly route (3x1 mins level 8-9 hill repeats mid ride, with 3 mins level 4 between) | **Thursday** Rest |
| **Friday** Level 5-6 for 80 mins on a rolling route, level 6-7 uphill in a gear slightly higher than feels comfortable | **Friday** Rest | **Friday** Rest | **Friday** Level 4 into 5-6 for 10 mins, time trial on test circuit, level 4 for 10 mins | **Friday** Level 5-6 for 90-120 mins on a rolling route, level 6-7 uphill in a gear slightly higher than feels comfortable | **Friday** Rest | **Friday** Rest | **Friday** Level 4 into 5-6 for 10 mins, time trial on test circuit, level 4 for 10 mins |
| **Saturday** Rest | **Saturday** Level 4 for 40 mins on a flat route (3x15 secs sprints mid ride, with 5 mins level 4 between) | **Saturday** Level 4 for 40 mins on a flat route (3x15 secs sprints mid ride, with 5 mins level 4 between) | **Saturday** Rest | **Saturday** Rest | **Saturday** Level 4 for 40 mins on a flat route (3x15 secs sprints mid ride, with 5 mins level 4 between) | **Saturday** Level 4 for 40 mins on a flat route (3x15 secs sprints mid ride, with 5 mins level 4 between) | **Saturday** Rest |
| **Sunday** Level 5-6 for 200 mins on a hilly route, level 7 uphill | **Sunday** Level 5-6 for 220 mins on a hilly route, level 7 uphill | **Sunday** Level 5-6 for 240 mins on a hilly route, level 7 uphill | **Sunday** Level 5 for 120 mins on a flat route | **Sunday** Level 5-6 for 180 mins on a hilly route, level 7 uphill | **Sunday** Level 5-6 for 200 mins on a hilly route, level 7 uphill | **Sunday** Level 5-6 for 120 mins on a rolling route, level 7 uphill | **Sunday** Level 5 for 120 mins on a flat route |

# Time trial plan

## Build speed endurance with this fast-paced race plan

The key physical ability for performing well in a time trial (a road race in which competitors start at intervals and cover the same course) is a high anaerobic threshold. This plan gives you a lot of work to push up the pace at which your body only just manages to keep up with recycling the lactic acid it produces. Go any harder and you won't be able to maintain your pace, so the other big time-trial ability is judging your pace. When you do each interval in this plan, practice exerting yourself evenly over the whole interval. There are lots of time-trial races all over Britain, just get in touch with your local cycling club for details. This plan is for races from ten to 25 miles. You need flat and rolling routes, plus a three-mile circuit for monthly progress-checking time trials.

### ■ Week 1

**Monday**
Ride at level 5-6 for 40 mins on a flat route

**Tuesday**
Rest

**Wednesday**
Level 5-6 for 50 mins on a flat route (2x10 mins at level 7 mid ride, with 5 mins level 4 between)

**Thursday**
Rest

**Friday**
Level 5-6 for 40 mins on a flat route (4x30 secs seated fast pedal mid ride, with 2 mins level 4 between)

**Saturday**
Rest

**Sunday**
Level 5-6 for 60 mins on a rolling route

### ■ Week 2

**Monday**
Rest

**Tuesday**
Level 5-6 for 60 mins on a rolling route (2x10 mins at level 7 mid ride, with 5 mins level 4 between)

**Wednesday**
Rest

**Thursday**
Level 5-6 for 60 mins on a flat route (2x10 mins at level 7 mid ride, with 5 mins level 4 between)

**Friday**
Rest

**Saturday**
Level 4 on a flat route for 40 mins (3x15 secs sprints mid ride, with 5 mins at level 4 between)

**Sunday**
Level 5-6 for 70 mins on a rolling route

### ■ Week 3

**Monday**
Rest

**Tuesday**
Level 5-6 for 70 mins on a rolling route (3x10 mins at level 7 mid ride, with 5 mins level 4 between)

**Wednesday**
Rest

**Thursday**
Level 5-6 for 70 mins on a flat route (3x10 mins at level 7 mid ride, with 5 mins level 4 between)

**Friday**
Rest

**Saturday**
Level 4 on a flat route for 40 mins (3x30 secs seated fast pedals mid ride, with 2 mins level 4) between)

**Sunday**
Level 5-6 for 80 mins on a flat route

### ■ Week 4

**Monday**
Level 5-6 for 50 mins on a rolling route

**Tuesday**
Rest

**Wednesday**
Level 5-6 for 60 mins on a flat route

**Thursday**
Rest

**Friday**
Level 4 for 10 mins, time trial on test circuit, level 4 for 10 mins

**Saturday**
Rest

**Sunday**
Rest or ride at level 4 for 40 mins on a flat route

### ■ Week 5

**Monday**
Level 5-6 for 60 mins on a rolling route (2x15 mins at level 7 mid ride, with 5 mins level 4 between)

**Tuesday**
Rest

**Wednesday**
Level 5-6 for 60 mins on a flat route (2x15 mins at level 7 mid ride, with 5 mins level 4 between)

**Thursday**
Rest

**Friday**
Level 5 for 50 mins on flat route (4x30 secs seated fast pedals mid ride, with 2 mins level 4 between)

**Saturday**
Rest

**Sunday**
Level 5 for 70 mins on a flat route

### ■ Week 6

**Monday**
Rest

**Tuesday**
Level 5-6 for 60 mins on a rolling route (20 mins at level 7 mid ride)

**Wednesday**
Rest

**Thursday**
Level 5-6 for 60 mins on a flat route (2x10 mins at level 7 – pushing to level 8 in last minute – mid ride, with 5 mins level 4 between)

**Friday**
Rest

**Saturday**
Level 4 for 40 mins on flat route (3x15 secs sprints mid ride, with 5 mins level 4 between)

**Sunday**
Level 5 for 80 mins on a flat route

### ■ Week 7

**Monday**
Rest

**Tuesday**
Level 5-6 for 60 mins on a flat route (3x5 mins at level 7 mid ride – pushing to level 8 in last minute – with 5 mins level 4 between)

**Wednesday**
Rest

**Thursday**
Level 5 for 60 mins on hilly route, level 6-7 uphill

**Friday**
Rest

**Saturday**
Level 4 for 40 mins on flat route (3x30 secs seated fast pedals mid ride, with 2 mins at level 4 between)

**Sunday**
Level 5 for 90 mins on a flat route

### ■ Week 8

**Monday**
Level 4 for 40 mins on a flat route

**Tuesday**
Rest

**Wednesday**
Level 5-6 for 60 mins on a rolling route

**Thursday**
Rest

**Friday**
Level 4-5 for 10 mins, time trial on test circuit, level 4 for 10 mins

**Saturday**
Rest

**Sunday**
Level 5-6 for 60 mins on a flat route

### ■ Week 9

**Monday**
Level 5 for 50 mins on a rolling route, level 6-7 uphill

**Tuesday**
Rest

**Wednesday**
Level 5-6 for 60 mins on a flat route (4x5 mins at level 7 mid ride – pushing to level 8 in last minute – with 5 mins level 4 between)

**Thursday**
Rest

**Friday**
Level 5-6 for 60 mins on flat route (4x30 secs fast pedals mid ride, with 2 mins at level 4 between)

**Saturday**
Rest

**Sunday**
Level 5 for 90 mins on rolling route, level 6-7 uphill

### ■ Week 10

**Monday**
Rest

**Tuesday**
Level 5 for 60 mins on rolling route (20 mins at level 7 mid ride)

**Wednesday**
Rest

**Thursday**
Level 5-6 for 60 mins on a flat route (3x3 mins at level 8 mid ride, with 3 mins level 4 between)

**Friday**
Rest

**Saturday**
Level 5-6 for 60 mins on a flat route (5x1 mins at level 9 mid ride, with 2 mins level 4 between)

**Sunday**
Level 5 for 60 mins (20 mins at level 7 mid ride)

### ■ Week 11

**Monday**
Rest

**Tuesday**
Level 5-6 for 60 mins on a flat route (4x5 mins at level 7 mid ride – pushing to level 8 in last minute – with 5 mins level 4 between)

**Wednesday**
Rest

**Thursday**
Level 5 on rolling route (middle 20 mins at level 6-7)

**Friday**
Rest

**Saturday**
Level 5-6 for 60 mins on a flat route (5x1 mins at level 9 mid ride, with 2 mins level 4 between)

**Sunday**
Level 5 for 60 mins, (20 mins at level 7 mid ride)

### ■ Week 12

**Monday**
Level 4 for 40 mins on a flat route

**Tuesday**
Rest

**Wednesday**
Level 5 for 40 mins on a flat route

**Thursday**
Rest

**Friday**
Level 4-5 for 10 mins, time trial on test circuit, level 4 for 10 mins

**Saturday**
Rest

**Sunday**
Rest or ride at level 4 for 40 mins on a flat route

# Top 10 cyclosportives

## Put your training to the test with these open to all bike races

**Cape Argus Cycle Tour, March**
The largest timed bike race in the world attracts about 35,000 riders each year to the 109km course that weaves along South Africa's spectacular Cape Argus peninsula. There's usually a few hundred British riders and the average finishing time is just over four hours.
cycletour.co.za

**Etape du Dales, May**
The name may sound French, but this is a steadfastly British event that takes place in the Yorkshire Dales. The 176km course takes about eight hours to complete and involves over 2,600m of ascents, often along narrow, winding roads. Even the descents are testing, with organisers warning that the ride down to Dentdale is both 'steep and dangerous'.
etapedudales.co.uk

**Fred Whitton Challenge, May**
At 180km and with 3,800m of ascents, this Lake District race, which starts and finishes at Coniston, really is a challenge. The highest point, the 454m Kirkstone Pass, comes early and the route includes six of the area's highest passes. There are also plenty of other steep inclines late on, including the brutal Hardknott Pass.
fredwhittonchallenge.org.uk

**Etape Caledonia, May**
Britain's only closed-road cyclosportive was launched in 2007. You don't have to battle with cars for the road, but thanks to the 130km route and 1,949m of climbing, you'll have to fight fatigue. The race starts and finishes in Pitlochry, Highland Perthshire and the route takes

Etape Caledonia

you through the dramatic countryside surrounding Loch Rannoch.
etapecaledonia.co.uk

**Tour Of Wessex, May**
There are plenty of different distances on offer during this Somerset-based three-day event, with 42km, 89km and 153km routes on the first day. There's a 166km race on day two, a 210km slog on day three and, if you're really after a challenge, you can do the main ride on each of the three days, adding up to a leg and lung busting 527km.
tourofwessex.com

**Forest Of Dean Spring Classic, May**
Good mid-distance race, with 2,370m of climbs over the 136km course. The ascents vary from gentle three milers to sterner leg stingers at an incline of about 25 per cent. The course starts and finishes in Monmouth.
forestofdeanspringclassic.co.uk

**Iron Mountain Sportive, June**
Staged in the shadow of the Iron

Mountain in Wales, this race starts and finishes in Abergavenny. There are three distances on offer: a beginner-friendly 40km, a testing 80km and an energy-sapping 180km. The long route starts easy, but gets more challenging, with the second 90km lap forcing you up a 500m mountain ascent.
abergavennyfestivalofcycling.co.uk

**Dave Lloyd Mega Challenge, June**
At 225km, the main route certainly lives up to its name. It involves a staggering 5,000m of climbs, the hardest of which are late on in the race. An easier 112km route is also on offer, with the hard work coming in the first half. Both routes start and finish in Ruthlin, North Wales.
davelloydmegachallenge.com

**Étape du Tour, July**
The race traces the exact route of one of the stages of the Tour de France. The stage changes from year to year, but they rarely pick an easy one. Usually they go for a 170km mountain route in the Alps or Pyrenees, such as the Pau to Hautacam stage. Expect plenty of climbs and several thousand Frenchmen jostling for position.
letapedutour.com

**Ride The Route, August**
Aping the Étape du Tour by tracing a stage of a big pro race, this event sees riders complete the stage of the Tour of Britain that runs from Worcester to Wolverhampton. The 162km route runs through the Malvern Hills and involves over 1,900m of ascents.
ridetheroute.net.

The Cape Argus Cycle
Tour in South Africa
attracts riders from
around the world

# Key cycling terms

### ■ Aerobic

Aerobic, meaning 'with air', exercise requires oxygen intake to fuel muscles for prolonged periods of activity, such as cycling and swimming.

### ■ Anaerobic

During anaerobic, meaning 'without air', exercise the body's requirement for energy exceeds that provided by respiration. Without oxygen, the muscles' ability to perform is dramatically reduced and can only function for short, intensive bursts, such as sprinting.

### ■ Apex

The middle or sharpest point in a curve. The apex of a corner is the middle or sharpest part of the corner.

### ■ Cadence

The number of complete revolutions per minute (rpm) of the pedal. Optimum cadence for efficiency and fitness is around 90-100rpm.

### ■ Carbon fibre

Lightweight material hardened by resin and used in bike frames.

### ■ Chainring

A toothed ring attached to the **cranks** that drives the chain and, in turn, the sprockets and the rear wheel of a bike.

### ■ Chainset

The construction of **chainrings** and **cranks**.

### ■ Cleat

A plate that attaches to the bottom of a cycling shoe to fix the rider's feet into an efficient pedalling position.

### ■ Clipless pedal

Pedal that attaches to the **cleat** on the bottom of cycling shoes.

### ■ Cool-down

A period of light-intensity exercise and stretching that lasts between five and 15 minutes following a period of more intense exercise. It aids the body's transition back to a resting state by lowering the heart rate and regulating breathing, and also removes lactic acid to aid muscle recovery.

### ■ Crank

The metal arms to which the pedals are attached.

### ■ Cyclosportive

Long distance cycling race, usually about 100 miles long, that is open to amateur riders. Some cyclosportives, such as the Etape du Tour, follow the same routes as professional races.

### ■ Derailleur gears

Mechanism that shifts the chain between **sprokets** on the rear wheel and between the **chainrings** attached to the **cranks**.

### ■ Downstroke

The movement of the rider pushing down on the pedal.

### ■ Drafting

To ride closely behind someone, getting into their slipstream to save energy.

### ■ Drivetrain

The construction of pedals, **chainset**, chain and **sprockets** that drives the bike forward, turning leg power into forward wheel revolution.

### ■ Drop handlebars

Road bike handlebars with ends that curve down and back towards the rider, allowing for a more aerodynamic riding position.

### ■ Fork

The two-pronged tube that holds the front wheel.

### ■ Gear

The **chainring** and **sprocket** system that is linked by the chain and dictates how easy or hard it is to turn the pedals.

### ■ Interval training

Alternating periods of high intensity exercise and low intensity exercise that provides greater cardiovascular gains than maintaining a constant pace. Interval sessions are demanding but should form a regular part of your training.

### ■ Head tube

A tube in the bike frame that supports the steer tube and the **fork**.

### ■ Lactic acid

A chemical compound of carbon, hydrogen, and oxygen that forms in hard-working muscles that, if levels become too high, results in performance deterioration and a burning sensation.

### ■ Mech

Short for mechanism. See **derailler gears**.

### ■ Panniers

Bags that you can attach to racks positioned at the sides of the bike's wheels.

### ■ Revolution

One full 360 degree turn of the **crank**.

### ■ Road race

Bike race on roads where all the riders start together, as opposed to a **time trial**, where riders go off at intervals.

### ■ Sprocket

A cog at the rear wheel that is turned by the chain.

### ■ Time Trial

Bike race where riders go off at intervals, as opposed to a **road race**, where riders start at the same time.

### ■ Warm-up

Low intensity exercise and stretching that lasts between five and 15 minutes and is done before more intense exercise. It helps prepare the body and mind for exercise by slowly warming the muscles and increasing heart rate.

# part 3

# Swim

Glide through the water with this technique and training masterclass

# Make a splash

## Dive into this section for everything you need to know about mastering swimming techniques and training to get fit in the pool

**S**wimming is an accessible sport. You hardly need any kit and because it's low impact it carries a low injury risk. But if you want to swim well, you'll need to concentrate on getting a good technique early on. That's because swimming is much more about technique than it is about raw power. This section focuses first on building sound swimming skills and then on using those skills to increase your fitness.

### How to use this section

You only need a small amount of kit before you get in the water, but wearing suitable trunks and goggles, and using training aids, can make your swims more enjoyable and productive. If you don't wear goggles, for example, you're unlikely to get your head down into the water, which makes it hard for you to achieve an efficient swimming position. The Gear pages (p110-111) run through the essential kit you'll need.

Good technique is absolutely vital in swimming and we explore front crawl in a step-by-step guide that breaks the arm cycle down into it's key stages. We also look at breaststroke

and backstroke in detail, as well as key skills, such as pushing of the wall and diving in. Part of perfecting your stroke involves practising swimming drills, which focus on a single aspect of your technique. These are outlined in the Drills section (p120-123), and are followed by the main training methods you can use to keep your pool sessions fresh and interesting.

Raw power isn't as important for swimming as it is for other sports, but

you do need good muscular endurance, particularly in key areas such as your lats (back muscles), which you use to propel yourself forwards. It's also crucial to have good core stability and flexibility so you can achieve full body rotation. If your core muscles are weak, you won't be able to rotate fully at the top of each arm pull, which will shorten your stroke and reduce your forward propulsion. Follow the stability and mobility workouts to make sure you can get your body into the most efficient position possible in the water.

Once you have mastered the swimming basics, the eight-week training plans in this section will continue to refine your skills and gradually build your fitness. Each session is designed to maximise the training effect you'll get for the time and effort you put in. None of the sessions involve large numbers of lengths at the same boring speed. Instead, you do a mixture of drills and strokes at varying intensities to help you stay motivated and to give you great results. We also provide a glossary (p146) to help you understand all of the terms used.

## Benefits of swimming

### ■ It's low impact

Resistance in swimming is created by the water, so the impact on your joints is minimal. That means you can do a lot of work without increasing your injury risk. That's important for beginners or people who have suffered from joint pain in the past, because their joints may lack stability. If you want to make your swim more resistance based, you can use hand paddles to make it more difficult to move your arms through the water.

### ■ It works your upper body

Running and cycling are good at developing lower-body strength and endurance but not so good at working your upper body. Swimming, on the other hand, is powered more by your upper than your lower body. By developing your shoulder muscles and your lats, swimming can help give you an athletic-looking V-shaped upper body. Your shoulders are easy to injure, but swimming is a low-risk way of developing that part of the body.

### ■ It's great for cross training

Swimming is a great sport to include as part of a cross-training regime because you can do it the day after performing another sport. Swimming doesn't put your body under huge amounts of stress, so you can intersperse swims with higher-impact activities, such as running, without giving your body another pounding. In fact, swimming is a good way of mobilising your joints the day after a demanding exercise session.

# Pool resources

The essential kit to help you swim better

### Swim costume

A pair of close-fitting trunks is all you need to get started in swimming, but if you are looking for ways to shave a fraction of a second off your personal best, you can now invest in hi-tech fabrics and full-body suits that will reduce drag and aid posture in the water.
**Pictured: Speedo Comme des Garçons brief, £43; Zoggs Cottesloe Hip Racer, £15.99; Speedo LZR Racer Jammer, £100**

### Cap and sandals

A swimming cap prevents drag, keeps hair free of chlorine and is a must for most competitive swims. Wear waterproof sandals around the pool edge and in showers to prevent the spread of fungal infections, such as athlete's foot.
**Pictured: Speedo Mizu pool shoes, £15; Aqua Sphere Classic swim cap, £3.99**

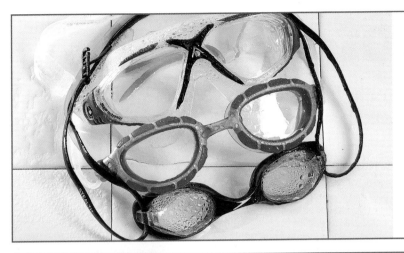

## Goggles

There are many types of goggles, from tiny, pared-down ones used by the pros, to mask-style goggles that provide good vision and are popular with open-water swimmers, such as triathletes. Whichever you choose, the main thing is fit, so try them to see if they sit comfortably on your face and seal well around the eyes. Anti-fogging solutions will help to keep goggles clear when you swim.

**Pictured: Aqua Sphere Vista, £18.99; Zoggs Predator Wiro-Frame, £13.99; Speedo Stealth, £10**

## Training aids

There are plenty of aids that help you with individual aspects of your stroke and target specific muscles. A kick board improves kick technique; the pull-buoy is held between the legs to hold your feet up while you concentrate on perfecting your arm stroke.

Swimming gloves and paddles give you a bigger surface area in the water, creating extra resistance and helping to build stronger muscles in the shoulders, chest and back.

**Pictured: Speedo Tech paddle, £10; Aqua Sphere fitness training gloves, £9.49; Zoggs Streamline kickboard, £10.60; Aqua Sphere pull-buoy, £6.99**

Stockists: Aqua Sphere, aquasphereswim.com, 01254 278873; Speedo, speedo.com, 0115 910 5267; Zoggs, zoggs.com

# Stroke of genius

## Work on your technique to stay injury-free and swim faster for longer with less effort

Good technique is immensely important in swimming, so it's vital to get into good habits early. Unlike running and cycling, where effort and speed are closely related, extra exertion in the pool won't automatically make you swim faster because swimming speed is more about efficiency than it is about brute force. The good news is that a sound technique lets you swim further and faster than you would when making the same effort with a poor stroke. Here you'll find a step-by-step guide to front crawl, as well as advice on breaststroke, backstroke and skills such as the diving start. First, though, you need to master the push-off start known as streamlining.

# Pushing off the wall

**S**treamlining, the position you should assume when pushing off the wall, is a key skill in swimming. You're aiming to get away from the wall in the most efficient body position possible. Solid streamlining technique cuts down the distance you have to swim each length, helping you to conserve energy and swim further.

### Arm position
Place one hand on top of the other with the thumb of the top hand clasped around the bottom hand. Extend your arms fully so they're cradling the back of your head rather than your ears. That stretches your lats (back muscles) and makes you thinner, so you'll travel efficiently through the water. You know you've got it right when your arms are extended but you've minimised the triangle of space between the top of your head and your wrists.

### Push off
Your momentum is generated from a squat off the wall. Lie flat in the water with your face and chest pointing down to the bottom of the pool. Place your feet, toes pointing towards the bottom of the pool, about shoulder width apart and bend your knees to 90°. Push through your feet to leave the wall. Tense your glutes to keep your legs high and prevent them from dropping down into the water and creating drag. Stay strong in your core throughout the move to maintain a long body shape.

### Follow through
You should be about a foot below the surface when you start travelling through the water. As you come up, take your first stroke as your body is about to break the surface.

# Front crawl
Nail the most popular stroke with this step-by-step guide

### ■ Body position
You want to have a flat, high body position because that creates the least amount of drag, which slows you down as you're moving through the water. If you lie flat in the water, the first part of your body to sink is your legs, so try to create balance by extending your arms and making sure you don't lift your head. Your head should be still throughout the stroke, unless you're breathing in. When you breathe, pivot your head to one side so that you look no higher than the gutter at the side of the pool.

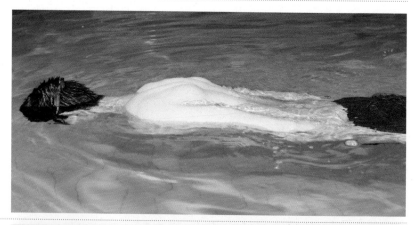

### ■ Upper-body rotation
Rotating your trunk during the stroke allows your powerful lat (back) muscles to initiate the stroke. Rotation should start from the shoulders and taper down the body so that your legs rotate only slightly. Your shoulders should rotate from one near-vertical position to the other, but don't get as far as 90°. Rotating properly will allow you to achieve a longer reach at the front of the stroke, which can help you swim faster and more efficiently. The key here is to imagine a spit running through your body and to rotate around that centre line.

### ■ Kick
Leg kick is responsible for about 10 per cent of your forward propulsion. It's important to get your kick right if you want to minimise drag. Leg kick should come from the hip flexors and glutes, rather than from the knee, and should be no deeper than the depth of your body. Your legs should be close together and as straight as possible. Keep your ankles relaxed and your feet extended for an efficient position.

### ◼ Breathing

Use bilateral breathing, which means you take a breath every third, fifth or seventh stroke. Taking a breath on alternate sides will help you to develop a symmetrical swimming stroke. It's important not to lift your head. Instead, rotate your neck to one side. You're aiming to cause the least possible disruption to your body position and balance.

### ◼ Arm cycle

#### 1 Hand entry

Your hand should enter the water in line with your shoulder, midway between your head and the full extension of your opposite arm. Pierce the water fingers first and rotate your body to let your hand reach your central bodyline.

#### 2 Arm extension

Once your hand enters the water it should be held palm facing downwards, and should travel forwards under and parallel to the surface of the water. When your arm is fully extended, your head should be tucked into your armpit with your bicep next to your head.

### 3 The catch

This is where the forward propulsion begins to take effect. Pivot at the elbow rather than the shoulder, and keep the hand and wrist firm so that the hand can be used as a paddle. Pulling from the shoulder increases your injury risk because you're trying to drag yourself through water using a small muscle group. Also, if you try to apply pressure from your shoulder with your arm extended, you're applying pressure downwards, which won't move you forwards.

### 4 Pull phase

This is the last third of the underwater phase. Your hand should pass down your central bodyline and accelerate as it goes. It should move in a slightly outward but predominantly backward motion. Imagine you're grabbing hold of the water and moving your body past your hand, instead of the other way round. Keep your hand close to the side of your body and finish the pull with your arm fully extended next to your hip.

### 5 Recovery

First to exit the water is your elbow. Keep it high with your hand travelling underneath. Upper-body rotation should help you maintain a high elbow. Your fingertips should be out of the water, close to your body and the surface. The recovery should be the relaxed part of the stroke.

### Timing

As your recovery arm passes by your head and begins the entry phase of the arm cycle, your extended arm should begin the catch phase of the cycle. This is known as 'near catch-up style'. Hand movement should go from slow to fast during the pull phase of the stroke. There are other variations of timing, but this method is effective if you're swimming for fitness.

# Breaststroke

### ■ The kick

Breaststroke kick generates over 50 per cent of your power. The most important thing is that both feet are doing the same thing at the same time. Start in a streamline position. Bend your knees to bring your heels up towards your backside, rather than bringing your knees up to your chest. As your heels come up, your knees separate slightly. At the same time, your ankles should rotate to turn your feet out so the soles are parallel to the surface of the water. Then pivot the knee round so your feet go around and back. This is now the propulsive phase so try to keep the resistance on the soles of your feet. Imagine grabbing the water with your feet and shoving it behind you. Exert the most force as your feet snap back, straightening out as they extend behind you. When your legs are together there should be a pause where you glide.

### ■ Arm cycle

As your knees begin to bend, your hands should push out into a 'Y' position. You want to avoid getting into an 'X' position with your feet out and your arms out. From the 'Y' position, bring your hands around your elbows, making sure they don't go past your shoulders. Your hands and forearms should work as paddles, pushing the water past you. Sweep your arms outwards and round to generate propulsion. Your hands then come back in towards your chin and chest, moving underneath your face before shooting back into the streamline position as your elbows squeeze in.

### ■ Breathing and head position

Make sure your head is down when you're gliding at the top of the stroke with your legs extended. Lift your head to breathe when your hands come back in towards your chest and push your head back down into the water as your hands shoot forward into the streamline position. When you're in the streamline, you should be looking at the bottom of the pool, not the direction you're heading.

# Backstroke

■ Lie on your back and don't tuck your chin into your chest. Lean back slightly into the water to counter your legs sinking and keep your head still throughout the stroke.

■ Use small kicks that come from the hips rather than the knees. Rotate your body every arm pull for efficiency and power.

■ Your arm should be straight during the recovery phase. Rotate your shoulders so you're reaching up towards the ceiling.

■ Your hand should enter the water in a line just outside your shoulder. Don't let your hand drift across and enter in line with the centre of your head. Your hand should enter the water little finger first.

■ Once your hand has reached a strong, deep catch position (extended and about two feet into the water, reaching for the bottom corner of the end of the pool you're swimming towards), bend your elbow and position your palm so it's facing the wall you're swimming away from. Try to avoid dropping your elbow when you bend it, and push the water towards your feet as your body rotates to the opposite side.

■ Your arms should work simultaneously, with one performing a strong pull under the water while the other performs a relaxed recovery above the water.

# Diving start

■ Start with your feet shoulder-width apart, your toes over the edge of the pool and your knees bent slightly.

■ Reach down with your fingers so that they touch your toes. Keep your head down, either looking down or behind you. Bend your knees slightly with your weight on the balls of your feet.

■ Throw your hands up and forward to create momentum (because your hands lead you into the water), then dive forwards.

■ As your fingers pierce the water, your body should be in a straight line with your legs together and your arms together. Your head should still be looking down. If it comes up you're more likely to belly flop.

■ Try to get your whole body travelling through the same small area in the water that you pierced with your fingertips. Keep your legs straight and together with your toes pointed.

■ Go about two feet deep and straighten as soon as your toes enter the water. Once your feet are in the water, hold the streamlined position for a moment to take advantage of the 'free' movement then start a freestyle kick to help push back up towards the surface. Start your arm cycle just as your forehead is about to break the surface of the water.

# Front crawl drills

Practise these skills to obtain a faster, more efficient stroke

Swimming drills are an essential part of improving technique. They focus on and develop particular aspects of the stroke, so you can iron out weaknesses. Do these drills as part of your warm-up or incorporate them into your main training set and intersperse them with lengths of normal swimming, so you get used to relating the drill skill back to the full stroke. Even when you're happy with your stroke, you should still practice drills to make sure you don't slip back into bad habits.

### Kicking with board

**Benefit:** Improves kicking technique.

**How to do it:** While holding a float out in front of you, kick from the hips, taking care not to go deeper than the depth of your body.

**Variation:** Basic kick drill.
Streamline off the wall and, with your legs outstretched and your arms tight to your ears, perform 10-15 kicks underwater. Don't rush into the kick. Use your momentum from streamlining and start a small kicking motion initiated from the hips. Kick no deeper than the depth of your body. When you need to breathe, stand up and swim back to the wall.

**Variation:** Vertical kicking.
In the deep end, place your hands on your thighs and kick your legs from the hip flexor muscles. Make sure the kick is only the depth of your body. Do four sets of ten seconds, increasing the length of the set as you improve.

## Catch-up

**Benefit:** Increases stroke length and elongates your body.

**How to do it:** Perform the regular front crawl stroke, but make sure that one of your arms is always extended and stationary while the other performs the stroke. When the working arm 'catches up' with the extended arm, swap roles.

**Variation:** Catch-up pull. Perform the catch-up drill, but with a pull-buoy between your legs. Keeping your legs straight and your toes pointed is key in order to target discrepancies in the pull.

## Basic extension drill

**Benefit:** Develops full upper body rotation.

**How to do it:** Practice the full rotation involved in front crawl, but only using the kick. Extend one arm out in front of you and hold the other by your side. Rotate the shoulder of your leading arm fully so it's under your chin, which will put you in the extension position. Alternate between lengths of left arm extended and right arm extended. Breathe every six kicks.

## Traditional single-arm

**Benefit:** Hones the arm cycle.

**How to do it:** With one arm stretched out in front of you, complete a full arm cycle with your opposite arm. Instead of switching arms repeat the arm cycle with the same arm and continue to do so for a set number of repetitions or distance. You could do three cycles with one hand or one length before performing the drill with your opposite hand. Always breathe away from the arm you're using.

**Variation:** Advanced single arm. Perform the single arm drill but with your non-working hand by your side. This makes the drill more difficult, but you can achieve full body rotation, so it's more authentic. Always breathe away from the arm you're using.

### Puppy paddle

**Benefit:** Improves the catch phase
of the arm cycle.

**How to do it:** Start with your head in
the water and both arms fully extended.
Then, one arm at a time, bend your elbow
to form the catch with your elbow high
and your fingertips pointing to the bottom
of the pool. Release the catch and bring
your forearm to the surface with the palm
angled upwards, before repeating with
the opposite arm. Remember to breathe
at regular intervals.

### Dog paddle
### catch-up style

**Benefit:** Develops the underwater phase
of the arm cycle.

**How to do it:** This drill involves
completing the underwater action.
With your head in the water and one
arm extended, your other arm should
complete the underwater propulsion
part of the stroke. Make sure you have a
high elbow in the catch position and pull
your hand down the centre line of your
body. Don't let your arm recover above
the water or pull your arm back. Instead,
slide your hand in towards your body
and, with your palm facing upwards, slide
up the centre line of your body towards
your other arm. Breathe, then repeat the
movement on the other side.

### Elbow pause

**Benefit:** Sharpens awareness of timing.

**How to do it:** With one arm extended in
front of your head, pause the recovering
arm when it's in line with the elbow of
your outstretched arm. After a one second
pause, rotate your body in line with the
arm that was paused and glide that arm
forwards so that the outstretched arm can
begin the catch phase of the stroke.

### Fingertip drag

**Benefit:** Promotes a high elbow position and hand awareness during recovery.

**How to do it:** Perform the regular front crawl stroke but don't let your fingertips leave the water during the recovery phase. Drag your fingers forwards through the water during the recovery phase, focusing on good body rotation and maintaining a high elbow position. Vary the drill from session to session by altering how much of your hand remains in the water.

### Fist/fingers open

**Benefit:** Develops your feel for the water.

**How to do it**

Perform the regular front crawl stroke but do it with either one or both of your hands in a fist. Try to press the water with the palm side of your forearm during the pull part of the stroke. After a few strokes, slowly unclench your fist, so your palm is open but not in the catch position. You should notice a difference in pressure on your hand. Keep your hand holding water as you move through the pull pattern of the stroke.

### Shark-fin drill

**Benefit:** Develops a high elbow in recovery.

**How to do it:** Swim regular front crawl but, when your arm is recovering, maintain a high elbow while tracing your thumb along the side of your body. Alternate between lengths of left arm shark fin and right arm shark fin.

# Varying your swims

## Use different training methods to give your swimming fitness a boost

**S**ticking to the same pace and number of lengths each session can be boring and won't maximise your fitness gains. Instead, introduce training methods such as interval and heart rate sessions that are developed to improve speed, endurance and technique. You also need to structure your time in the pool so that you avoid injury and prepare your body properly for the most demanding part of the session.

## How to structure your swim

The following breakdown is a guide to how you should weight your time in the pool and is based on a one-hour swimming session.

### ■ Warm-up
**10 per cent of total pool time**
This should be an easy swim to mobilise your joints and increase blood flow.

### ■ Subset
**25 per cent of total pool time**
An extension of the warm-up, a subset is designed to raise your heart rate and introduce skills that you need to practice while you're still fresh.

### ■ Main set
**55 per cent of total pool time**
The meat of the session and a sustained and structured period where your heart rate is elevated. A second subset may be added after the main set to extend the cool-down if you have completed a particularly intense main set.

### ■ Cool-down
**10 per cent of total pool time**
This should be an easy swim designed to reduce heart rate and flush out lactic acid.

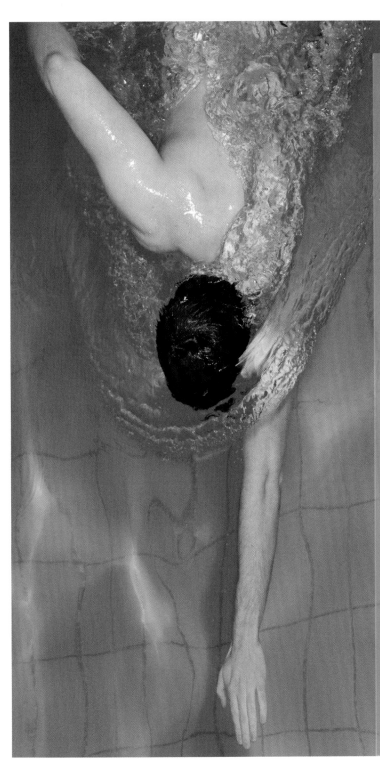

## Interval sessions

Interval sessions are periods of higher-intensity swimming punctuated by periods of recovery, and should form a substantial part of your training. They allow you to fit more challenging work into your session than if you tried to do it all continuously. The aim is to raise your heart rate during the periods of high effort so your body gets used to working at that intensity and can adapt to cope with the stress. There are several ways you can adjust the structure of your intervals to keep them fresh and make them progressively more difficult.

### ■ Distance
You can increase the distance of the interval and train yourself to swim further at the same high intensity. You could, for example, start in week one of your training programme by swimming 4x200 metres and increase that to 4x300 metres by week four.

### ■ Time
You can vary the time you have to complete an interval so that you swim a set distance in a progressively faster time. You could, for example, start by giving yourself two minutes to swim 100 metres in the first week of your training programme and increase the pace so that by the fourth week you're covering the same distance in one minute 50 seconds.

### ■ Number of repeats
As you improve, you can increase the number of repeats you swim during a session. You might, for example, start by being able to swim 5x100 metres front crawl in your first week before you reach exhaustion. By week four, you may be able to complete 8x100 metres before you tire yourself out.

### ■ Aim time
These intervals are structured so that you have a total interval time and an aim time by which you should complete the work in that interval. If you have a two minute interval with a one minute 45 seconds aim time, you would have 15 seconds rest. You can then reduce the aim time to swim at a faster pace but with more rest between repetitions.

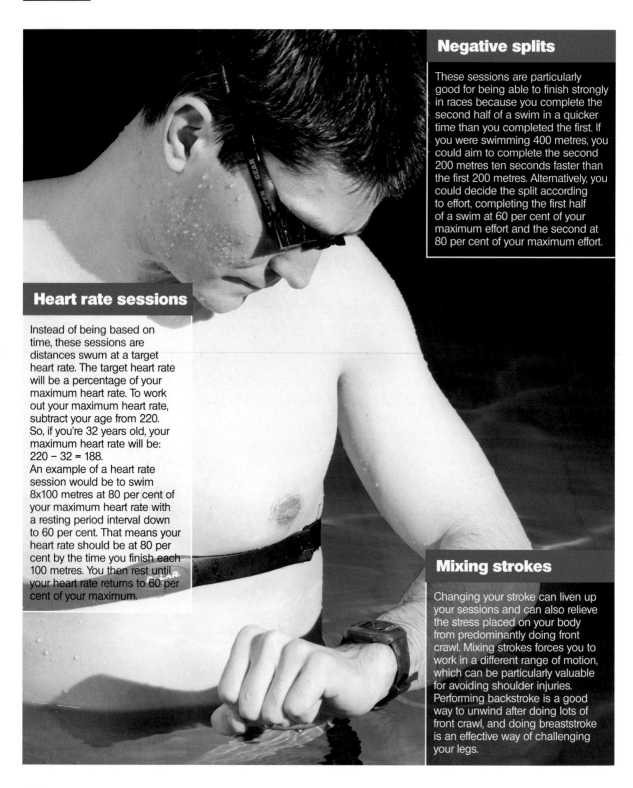

## Negative splits

These sessions are particularly good for being able to finish strongly in races because you complete the second half of a swim in a quicker time than you completed the first. If you were swimming 400 metres, you could aim to complete the second 200 metres ten seconds faster than the first 200 metres. Alternatively, you could decide the split according to effort, completing the first half of a swim at 60 per cent of your maximum effort and the second at 80 per cent of your maximum effort.

## Heart rate sessions

Instead of being based on time, these sessions are distances swum at a target heart rate. The target heart rate will be a percentage of your maximum heart rate. To work out your maximum heart rate, subtract your age from 220. So, if you're 32 years old, your maximum heart rate will be: 220 − 32 = 188.
An example of a heart rate session would be to swim 8x100 metres at 80 per cent of your maximum heart rate with a resting period interval down to 60 per cent. That means your heart rate should be at 80 per cent by the time you finish each 100 metres. You then rest until your heart rate returns to 60 per cent of your maximum.

## Mixing strokes

Changing your stroke can liven up your sessions and can also relieve the stress placed on your body from predominantly doing front crawl. Mixing strokes forces you to work in a different range of motion, which can be particularly valuable for avoiding shoulder injuries. Performing backstroke is a good way to unwind after doing lots of front crawl, and doing breaststroke is an effective way of challenging your legs.

## Time and distance swims

A challenging alternative to interval training is to swim as far as you can in a fixed amount of time or to swim a set distance as quickly as possible. These overall times and distances can give you a useful indication of how well you're progressing. You can also break the sessions up by doing a pyramid swim, where you swim for one minute, two minutes, three minutes, four minutes and five minutes, with a one minute rest between sections, before going back down the other way. You can also reverse the pyramid and start by swimming for five minutes.

## Build swims

These sessions involve a gradual increase in pace and effort over a set distance. They're particularly useful for people wanting to enter races and triathlons because they teach you to control and to step up your pace. As you tire your instinct is to slow down, but build swims discipline you to maintain and even increase your pace. A typical build session could be 6x300 metres build front crawl. The first 300 metres could be swum at 60 per cent, the second at 70 per cent and the third at 80 per cent. That block would be repeated to complete the set. Build swims are similar to reducing or descending sets, meaning that you get quicker with each repeat.

## Broken swims

Aimed at improving your raw speed, broken swims are swum faster than race pace. You try to beat your best time for a distance by breaking it into shorter distances. A broken swim in a 25-metre pool would be 100 metres broken with 5 seconds at each length. If your best time for 100 metres is 80 seconds you aim to swim each length in under 20 seconds, with five seconds rest between lengths. If you want to make the session even more challenging, you could try to beat your best time by only taking a rest after the first 50 or 75 metres.

# Don't dive in

Do the following poolside warm-up before a swim to prepare your muscles and joints for the work to come

---

### 1 Trunk rotation
**Sets:** 1 **Reps:** 20

■ With your hands by your side and your head still, rotate your upper body.
■ Bring your front shoulder under your chin with each rotation.
■ Don't bring your chin down to meet your shoulder.
■ Keep your hips facing forward.

**Why do it?** Your head should be still during front crawl, apart from when you're breathing. The stroke is at it's most streamlined when your body is rotated to the side. This move gets your body used to working in both those ways.

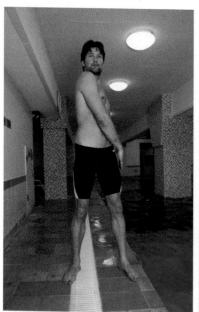

### 2 Arm circles
**Sets:** 1 **Reps:** 15 each side, each direction

■ Circle your left arm forwards through 360°, creating as big a circle as possible. Repeat 15 times.
■ Circle your left arm backwards through 360°, creating as big a circle as possible. Repeat 15 times.
■ Repeat sequence with your right arm.

**Why do it?** Shoulder joints are central to the main swimming strokes. This move activates the fluid in the joint to lubricate your movement.

### 3 Arm circles in opposite directions
**Sets:** 1 **Reps:** 15 each direction

■ Circle your left arm forward through 360°, creating as big a circle as possible.
■ At the same time, circle your right arm backwards through 360°.
■ After completing 15 reps, repeat the move with each arm going in the other direction.

**Why do it?** As well as warming up your shoulder joints, this move also increases mobility of your upper back muscles.

## 4  Calf stretch
**Sets:** 3 **Time:** 20 seconds

■ Hold onto the rail and stand with your toes on the top step.
■ Lower your heels into the water until you feel the stretch in your calves.

**Why do it?** This gives you a deep stretch in the calves and helps to get blood flowing into your lower leg, reducing your chances of suffering cramp.

## 5  Ankle circles
**Sets:** 1 **Reps:** 15 each direction, each side

■ Sit on the floor with your legs together and outstretched in front of you.
■ Lift one leg slightly and circle your ankle through 360° in one direction for 15 repetitions.
■ Repeat the movement in the opposite direction before switching legs and repeating the sequence.

**Why do it?** Increasing ankle flexibility will make it easier to point your toes as you swim, which reduces drag.

## 6  Towel grabber
**Sets:** 2 **Time:** 20 seconds

■ Sit on a chair with your feet on a towel. Try to grab the towel with your toes as you arch your feet.
■ When you have gripped the towel as firmly as you can, relax your feet and repeat the move.

**Why do it?** This move increases strength and flexibility in the arch of your foot, which will help reduce the risk of cramp when your toes are pointed.

# Strong swimmer

## Develop strength and stability in key swimming muscles to maximize stroke efficiency and power

**S**wimming speed and endurance demands an efficient stroke. But unless you're strong enough and stable enough to get your body into the right position in the water, you won't be able to maximize efficiency. This workout targets the lats and triceps – key muscles used in swimming, particularly front crawl. It also develops a strong core, which will help prevent your legs from dropping down into the water and causing drag. Perform the following exercises in order and do this workout twice a week on non-swimming days.

### 1 Lat pull-down

**Sets: 3 Reps: 12**

■ Use a wide grip on the bar.
■ Retract your shoulder blades and keep your torso upright.
■ Pull the bar down in front of your upper chest.
■ Resist the temptation of leaning back too far to aid the movement.

**Why do it?** Strong lats give you a strong front crawl, with more power in the propulsion phase of the stroke.

## 2 Cable kick-back
**Sets:** 3 **Reps:** 12 each side

■ Keep your body horizontal and your upper arm in line with your body.
■ Rest your hand on the bench underneath your shoulder.
■ Make sure there is tension on the cable at the beginning of the move.
■ Squeeze your triceps at the top of the move.

**Why do it?** This move strengthens your triceps, which gives you more power at the end of the underwater phase of the front crawl.

## 3 Plank
**Sets:** 3 **Time:** 20-40 seconds

■ Hold your body in a straight line from head to heels.
■ Position your elbows beneath your shoulders.

**Why do it?** By increasing your core stability, this exercise enables you to kick using small movements from the hips and to rotate your body around a central axis without twisting.

## 4 Side plank
**Sets:** 3 **Time:** 20-40 seconds each side

■ Hold your body in a straight line from head to feet.
■ Position your elbow directly beneath your shoulder.

**Why do it?** This gives you similar gains to the plank, but targets your internal and external obliques, which will keep you stable when you rotate your body.

## 5 Internal cable rotation
**Sets:** 3 **Reps:** 12 each side

■ Stand side on to a cable set at
waist height.
■ Keep your upper arm by your side.
■ Rotate your arm inwards.

**Why do it?** This move targets the rotator
cuff muscles in your shoulder, which are
prone to injury from overuse in swimming
or from poor technique.

## 6 External cable rotation
**Sets:** 3 **Reps:** 12 each side

■ Stand side on to a cable set at
waist height.
■ Keep your elbow bent at 90°.
■ Rotate your arm outwards.

**Why do it?** This move targets the easy-
to-injure rotator cuffs in your shoulders
from a different angle.

# Fluid movements

Focus on improving your mobility and flexibility to achieve a better swimming technique

If you're inflexible, you may struggle to achieve the most efficient body positions in the water. Poor shoulder rotation and tight lats mean your catch and pull will come from your shoulders rather than your strong lats. If that happens, your stroke will be shorter and less powerful, and you'll increase your risk of injury. If you're a runner or cyclist, you may have inflexible ankles, which can cause drag and slow you down. The ankle circles will help you to point your toes while you swim and the calf stretch will guard against cramp caused by holding your feet in that position. Perform these moves in order and do this routine twice a week on non-swimming days.

## 1 Streamline body position

**Sets** 3 **Time:** 20 seconds

■ Stand with your feet together.
■ Raise your arms above your head with one hand on top of the other.
■ Position your biceps so they're against the backs of your ears.

**Why do it?** This position mimics the one you should get into every time you push off from the wall, which helps you travel further with less effort.

## 2 Lats stretch
**Sets** 3 **Time:** 20 seconds each side

■ Kneel down and extend one arm out
so it rests on the floor.
■ Press down on your arm to feel the
stretch down your side.

**Why do it?** This move helps you to reach
forward fully in the water, extending your
stroke to give you a longer pull.

## 3 Triceps stretch
**Sets** 3 **Time:** 20 seconds each side

■ Bend your arm at the elbow and drop
it down behind your back.
■ With your other arm, push down gently
on your elbow until you feel the stretch in
your triceps.

**Why do it?** Your triceps provide the
majority of the power at the end of the
underwater phase of the front crawl,
so you need to keep them flexible to
avoid post-session stiffness.

### 4 Dry land kicking
**Sets** 3 **Time:** 20 seconds

■ Lie on your front with your head resting on your folded arms.
■ Point your toes, engage your core and tighten your glutes.
■ Kick your legs as if you were swimming, so kick from the hip not the knee.

**Why do it?** This exercise teaches you to kick from the hip rather than the knee, promoting a better kicking action.

### 5 Kneeling ankle stretch
**Sets** 5 **Time:** 5, 10, 15, 20, 25 seconds

■ Kneel down, resting your buttocks on your heels with your toes pointing out behind you. Hold for five seconds. Relax then repeat, adding five more seconds to each set until you reach 25 seconds.

**Why do it?** By improving your ankle mobility, this move allows you to kick with your toes pointing away from you, which reduces drag.

### 6 Sitting ankle stretch
**Sets** 3 **Time:** 20 seconds

■ Sit on the floor with your legs together and outstretched in front of you.
■ Point your toes away from you to stretch the front of your ankles.

**Why do it?** Doing this move will reduce your chances of getting cramp when you swim with your toes pointed.

# Training aids

Use these easy to apply techniques and principles to get an edge

## Kick with and without floats

All kicking drills should be done with and without a float. Without a float you can practice combining a good kick with upper-body rotation and the full extension position. With a float, you focus solely on getting the leg action correct.

### Drill quality not quantity
Swimming drills should be done over short distances with plenty of rest, because their aim is to build technique rather than stamina. If you find the drill difficult, mix it up with conventional strokes. Half a length of a good drill is better than doing a full length with poor technique.

### Double your trunks
Wearing two pairs of baggy trunks might make you look a bit odd, but the increased drag will make your training more demanding without having to sacrifice technique. When you go back to your normal pair or a racing suit you'll find it easier.

### Combine drills with strokes
Don't just perform a drill on it's own. Do a drill and then perform the full stroke, taking care to concentrate on the drill aspect of the stroke. This will help you assimilate the drill's key technique back into your full stroke.

### Keep your distance
Making sure there's a five-second gap between you and the swimmer in front will mean that you don't cheat by getting towed along in their slipstream. If you want to be completely sure that there's no draft from the person in front, leave a ten second gap.

### Don't stop drilling
Even if you feel confident in your stroke technique, you should still practice

drills. Do them as part of your warm-up or cool-down to make sure that your arm pull, recovery and rotation are performed naturally when you're doing your full stroke.

### Limit your paddle use
Paddles are a useful training aid, but don't use them for more than about 25 per cent of the time you're in the pool. The increased resistance they create can, with overuse, heighten your risk of shoulder injury.

### Focus on one element
When practising a drill, always concentrate on one aspect of the stroke, such as the recovery. This will help reduce the feeling of being overwhelmed from having to think about several components at once.

### Breathe bilaterally for fitness
Using a bilateral breathing pattern will improve your fitness, as well as help keeping your stroke balanced. Breathing every third stroke rather then every second stroke means you take one third fewer breaths per length so you learn to go further on the same number of breaths. Doing a tumble turn at the end of each length will also help because you take your last breath of the length a metre before the wall and, you don't take another breath for several metres.

### Don't breathe before turns
Avoiding breathing just before and just after a turn will increase your fitness as your body adapts to cope with the added strain. At the end of the pool, you will often see the lane ropes change from blue to white or a solid red colour for about three metres. Try to avoid taking a breath after the point where the colours change.

### Build speed throughout lengths
Increasing your pace throughout a length will help alleviate the boredom of doing laps. Finishing a length at speed also means you carry pace into the tumble turn, which will help you get more distance off the wall.

### Don't stop short
Stopping a couple of metres short of a full length at the end of a set, either through laziness or because someone is in the way, is a lot of missed distance each year. Swim through the offending swimmer to complete the length and they'll soon get the message.

# Fast lane fitness

## Follow these structured plans to make rapid swimming progress

Swim training is the same as any other sport: if you only ever do the same thing in practice, such as endless easy lengths, you'll only ever get better at doing that one thing. After a while, you won't make any progress at all because your body will adapt to cope with the familiar stimulus. To carry on improving, you need to challenge your cardiovascular and muscle systems by putting them under different physical stresses. You can do that by following a plan that gradually increases the distance and intensity required to complete the work.

If you look at these two plans (one for beginners and one for more advanced swimmers) and think that they'll take too much effort to follow, think about this: by sticking to them, you'll be saving yourself time and energy because they've been constructed to maximise the fitness and technique benefits you get from your time in the water. Both plans have been created by Dan Bullock, head coach at swim tuition specialists SwimForTri (swimfortri.com), and are based on the formats they use for one-on-one sessions.

## How to use these plans

The length counts in the plans are for a 33-metre pool so three lengths equal about 100 metres. If you swim in a different length pool, adjust your lengths accordingly.

For the main set, do as much as possible until you get to ten minutes before you plan to exit the pool and move on to the cool down.

**KEY TO ABBREVIATIONS**
**3L:** three lengths
**2x3L:** two blocks of three lengths. The blocks will usually be separated by a rest period
**70%:** 70 per cent of your maximum effort
**Choice stroke:** you choose what stroke you perform
**Easy:** swim at a comfortable pace

For other unfamiliar terms, see the glossary on pages 146-147. For descriptions of drills, see pages 120-123.

### Warm-up
It's essential to warm up before a session to mobilise your joints and raise your heart rate. Start by doing the poolside mobility exercises described on p128-129. Then do the following pool-based warm up: 200 metres choice stroke then 3x2L as 2L at 50%, 2L at 60% and 2L at 70% with 20 seconds rest every two lengths.

### Cool-down
At the end of your session, you should cool down to reduce your heart rate and flush lactic acid out of your muscles. Do 200 metres easy choice stroke or drills.

*To find out more about SwimForTri's bespoke swim coaching services, visit swimfortri.com.*

# Beginners training plan

## This progressive training plan has been designed to fit into two sessions a week and will build your swimming fitness

If you're new to swimming or want to nail your technique before moving on to a more challenging programme, this plan is for you. Each session involves a warm-up and a subset where you practice key drills and skills. This is followed by the main set, which is where you'll challenge yourself physically, concentrating on a training method or aspect of technique each session. Finish with a cool-down to prepare yourself for your next swim.

The plan should improve all elements of your swimming, setting you a series of short-term goals designed to make you emerge, after eight weeks, as a competent swimmer with a sound stroke.

| Week | Session 1 | Session 2 |
|---|---|---|
| 1 | **Subset:** 6x1L with fins, resting for 20 seconds between lengths. Odd lengths, choice drill. Even lengths, build front crawl.<br>200 metres easy, alternate lengths backstroke and breaststroke.<br><br>**Main set:** 6L front crawl at 60%, then 3L choice drill. Rest for 1 minute and repeat. | **Subset:** 200 metres front crawl. Swim as 2L build, 1L fast. Repeat.<br>200 metres advanced single-arm drill.<br><br>**Subset:** 4L front crawl at 75%, then 2L pull. Rest for 20 seconds and repeat. |
| 2 | **Subset:** 2L front crawl with arms in streamline position, 2L with kickboard, 2L front crawl kick in extension position. All done with fins.<br>200 metres, alternate lengths backstroke and breaststroke.<br><br>**Main set:** 6x3L with fins, 30 seconds rest between blocks. Swim each block as 1L advanced single-arm with left arm, 1L advanced single-arm with right arm, 1L front crawl. | **Subset:** 3x2L, odd lengths 60%, even lengths 80%. Similar stroke count on all lengths. Rest for 1 minute between blocks.<br>200 metres alternate lengths backstroke and breaststroke.<br><br>**Main set:** 400 metres front crawl catch-up style at 70%, then rest for 1 minute. 300 metres pull with paddles at 75%, then rest for 1 minute. 200 metres kick with float and fins, then rest for 1 minute. 100 metres easy front crawl. |

**■ Fins**
Some of the sessions involve fins, which let you slow down the stroke to focus on technique.
**Pictured: Speedo fins £15**

# Beginners training plan

| Week | Session 1 | Session 2 |
|------|-----------|-----------|
| **3** | **Subset:** 4x100 metres choice drills. Use a different stroke or drill for each 100 metres. Rest for 1 minute every 100 metres.<br>100 metres alternate lengths backstroke and breaststroke kick with float.<br><br>**Main set:** 3x300 metres with 45 seconds rest between each 300 metres. Swim the first 300 as fingertip drag drill at 50%, the second at 60% with paddles and the third front crawl at 70%. Count strokes for each length and aim to be consistent. | **Subset:** 6x1L with 10 seconds rest between lengths. Start at 40% for the first length and build to 90%.<br>200 metres easy catch-up with a pull buoy.<br><br>**Main set:** 200 metres with paddles at 65%, then rest for 1 minute. 200 metres as 2L controlled, 1L hard, then rest for 1 minute and repeat. 200 metres near-catch-up with fingertip drag and fins at 75%. 200 metres easy choice stroke. |
| **4** | **Subset:** 6x1L. Swim as two blocks of 1L pull without a float, 1L choice drill, 1L build. Rest for 20 seconds between blocks.<br>200 metres with front crawl legs and breaststroke arms.<br><br>**Main set:** 4x100 metres at 70%. Swim as 2x100 metres front crawl and 2x100 metres of pull with paddles. Rest for 20 seconds between each 100 metres.<br>4x2L at 75%, swum as 2x2L front crawl and 2x2L pull with paddles. Rest for 10 seconds every 2L.<br>4x1L at 85%. Rest for 5 seconds between lengths. | **Subset:** 6x1L. Swim as two blocks of three lengths, building speed within blocks. Rest for 15 seconds between lengths.<br><br>**Main set:** 300 metres front crawl catch-up with pull buoy at 75%, then rest for 1 minute. 300 metres front crawl with paddles at 75%, then rest for 1 minute. 300 metres front crawl with fins at 75%, then rest for 1 minute. 100 metres easy front crawl. |
| **5** | **Subset:** 4x100 metres front crawl, resting for 15 seconds between each 100 metres. Swim as 2x100 metres with a pull buoy and 2x100 metres with paddles. Do one 100 metres at 40%, one at 50%, one at 60% and one at 70%. You choose the order.<br>200 metres choice drills.<br><br>**Main set:** 3x100 metres front crawl pull with paddles at 60%. Rest for 20 seconds between each 100 metres.<br>2x100 metres front crawl near-catch-up with fingertip drag at 70% with fins. Rest for 45 seconds between each 100 metres.<br>100 metres front crawl at 80% with fins. | **Subset:** 6x1L with 10 seconds rest between lengths. Start at 40% for the first length and build to 90% by the last.<br>200 metres easy catch-up with a pull buoy.<br><br>**Main set:** 200 metres with paddles at 65%, then rest for 1 minute.<br>200 metres as 2L controlled, 1L hard. Rest for 1 minute and repeat.<br>200 metres near-catch-up with fingertip drag and fins at 75%.<br>200 metres easy choice stroke. |

| Week | Session 1 | Session 2 |
|---|---|---|
| **6** | **Subset:** 12x1L front crawl. Swim as 3 blocks of 4 lengths with 15 seconds rest between blocks. For each block, swim the first length as catch-up, the second at 80%, the third as catch-up and the fourth as 80%.<br><br>**Main set:** 2L front crawl then 1L choice stroke. Repeat 8 times. | **Subset:** 6x1L front crawl with fins, resting for 10 seconds between lengths. Odd lengths, streamline from the wall and swim half a length with kicks before finishing with easy front crawl. Even lengths, build from easy to hard.<br><br>**Main set:** 5L swum as 3L 60-80% choice stroke straight into 2L single-arm drill with alternate arms for each length. Repeat 6 times, resting for 45 seconds between blocks. |
| **7** | **Subset:** 6x1L single-arm drill, resting for 20 seconds between lengths.<br><br>**Main set:** 7L front crawl at 65% straight into 2L fast front crawl, then rest for 1 minute. 4L front crawl at 75% straight into 2L fast front crawl. Rest for 1 minute, then repeat. 2L front crawl at 80% straight into 1L easy front crawl. Rest for 30 seconds, then repeat twice. 100 metres easy front crawl with fingertip-drag drill and fins. | **Subset:** 6x1L kick with fins. Odd lengths, no float and hands in streamline. Even lengths, on back with hands by side. Rest for 45 seconds between lengths. 200 metres choice stroke.<br><br>**Main set:** 4x300 metres front crawl. Increase effort so that first 300 metres is at 60% and the fourth is at 80%. Swim 2x300 metres with a pull buoy and 2x300 metres with paddles. You choose the order. Rest for 1 minute between each 300 metres. |
| **8** | **Subset:** 200 metres without rest as 2 blocks of three lengths. Swim length 1 backstroke, length 2 breaststroke, length 3 front crawl. Build from 70% to 90% within lengths.<br><br>**Main set:** 400 metres pull at 60%, then rest for 30 seconds. 200 metres front crawl at 80%, then rest for 30 seconds. 200 metres front crawl at 60%, then rest for 30 seconds. 400 metres front crawl at 80%. | **Subset:** 2L front crawl, 1L either backstroke or breaststroke. Repeat four times. 200 metres easy breaststroke arms with front crawl legs.<br><br>**Main set:** 400 metres front crawl at 80%. Record your time. 200 metres easy front crawl. 400 metres front crawl at 60% with fins. 200 metres strong front crawl. Time yourself and aim to be 5 seconds faster than half your 400-metre time. |

# Advanced plan

Do this testing, two-sessions-a-week plan to make waves
with your swimming fitness

This plan is aimed at swimmers who have completed the beginner programme or who already have good swimming technique and fitness. The format remains the same, but the distance, intensity and difficulty of the drills has been stepped up. Even at this stage, executing drills as correctly as possible is vital. They give your mind and body a chance to really focus on what you're doing and prevent you from slipping into bad habits, something that's easily done when you're tired or working at a high intensity. At the end of the eight weeks, you should be a strong swimmer with a powerful, efficient stroke.

# Advanced plan

Build your speed endurance with this eight-week plan

| Week | Session 1 | Session 2 |
|---|---|---|
| **1** | **Subset:** 200 metres non-front crawl. 4x2L front crawl with 15 seconds rest between blocks.<br><br>**Main set:** 200 metres front crawl pull with paddles at 60%, then rest for 1 minute. 200 metres front crawl catch-up drill at 70%, then rest for 1 minute. 200 metres front crawl pull with paddles at 60%, then rest for 1 minute. 200 metres front crawl with fins at 70%, then rest for 1 minute. | **Subset:** 200 metres choice drills. 6x1L shark-fin drill. Swim as 1L left arm recovering, 1L right arm recovering.<br><br>**Main set:** 300 metres front crawl with a pull buoy, then rest for 40 seconds. 200 metres catch-up drill with fins, then rest for 40 seconds. 12x1L alternate backstroke and breaststroke, resting for 20 seconds between lengths. 300 metres catch-up drill with a pull buoy. |
| **2** | **Subset:** 200 metres choice stroke. 100 metres front crawl. 200 metres choice stroke. All at 80%. 200 metres kicking drills.<br><br>**Main set:** 4L front crawl at 70% straight into 2L catch-up, then rest for 30 seconds. 200 metres pull with paddles, then rest for 45 seconds. 4L front crawl at 70% straight into 2L backstroke then rest for 30 seconds. 200 metres pull with paddles then rest for 45 seconds. 4L front crawl at 70% straight into 2L pull, then rest for 30 seconds. 200 metres pull with paddles, then rest for 45 seconds. | **Subset:** 6x1L dog-paddle drill, resting for 10 seconds between lengths. 200 metres breaststroke arms with front crawl legs<br><br>**Main set:** 200 metres pull at 70%. 100 metres build. Swim first length at 60% building to third length at 80%, then rest for 1 minute. 100 metres advanced single-arm drill. Repeat the set two more times. |

# Advanced plan

| Week | Session 1 | Session 2 |
|---|---|---|

**3**

**Session 1**

**Subset:** 3x200 metres with fins, resting for 30 seconds between each 200 metres. Swim odd lengths backstroke, even lengths build front crawl from 40% to 80% within each length.

**Main set:** 3x400 metres, resting for 60 seconds between each 400 metres. Swim as 200 metres pull with float and paddles, 100 metres front crawl kick with breaststroke arms, 100 metres build 60% to 80%.

**Session 2**

**Subset:** 200 metres front crawl, then rest for 1 minute. Swim lengths 3 and 6 build to fast. 2x3L with float, resting for 30 seconds between blocks. Swim as 1L backstroke kick, 1L breaststroke kick, 1L front crawl kick.

**Main set:** 2x600 metres front crawl. Swim as 400 metres build from 50%, increasing effort by 10% every 100 metres straight into 200 metres hard with paddles.

**4**

**Session 1**

**Subset:** 12x1L swum as 3 blocks of 4 lengths with 10 seconds rest between blocks. Swim as 1L at 50%, 1L at 60%, 1L at 70% and 1L at 80%.
200 easy choice stroke

**Main set:** 4x300 metres front crawl, resting for 1 minute between each 300 metres. Swim as 200 metres at 65%, then 100 metres at 75%.

**Session 2**

**Subset:** 2x100 metres, resting for 40 seconds between each 100 metres. Swim first 100 metres as 1L backstroke kick, 1L breaststroke and 1L front crawl kick. Swim second 100 as 1L backstroke, 1L breaststroke kick, 1L front crawl. All without floats.
200 easy catch-up drill with a pull buoy.

**Main set:** 5x200 metres. Swim each 200 metres as 4L build within lengths, 2L backstroke. Rest for 45 seconds between blocks.
200 metres with fins at 60%.

**5**

**Session 1**

**Subset:** 4x100 metres front crawl with 15 seconds rest between each 100 metres. Swim first 100 at 40%, second 100 at 60%, third 100 at 80% and fourth easy.
200 metres catch-up drill.

**Main set:** 6x200 metres at 75%, resting for 30 seconds between each 200 metres.

**Session 2**

**Subset:** 6x1L, resting for 15 seconds between lengths. Odd lengths, breaststroke arms with front crawl legs. Even lengths, front crawl.

**Main set:** 600 metres front crawl, hard every third length then rest for 1 minute.
100 metres easy catch-up, then rest for 30 seconds. 400 metres front crawl, hard every third length then rest for 1 minute. 100 metres easy catch-up then rest for 30 seconds.
200 metres front crawl, even lengths hard then rest for 1 minute.
100 metres easy catch-up drill.

| Week | Session 1 | Session 2 |
|---|---|---|
| **6** | **Subset:** 12x1L swum in 3 blocks of 4 lengths with 10 seconds rest between blocks. Swim each block as 1L front crawl catch-up, 1L backstroke, 1L front crawl catch-up, 1L backstroke.<br><br>**Main set:** Pyramid set. 1 minute swim, 1 minute rest, 2 minutes swim, 1 minute rest, 3 minutes swim, 1 minute rest, 4 minutes swim, 1 minute rest, 3 minutes swim, 1 minute rest, 2 minutes swim, 1 minute rest, 1 minute swim. | **Subset:** 6x1L, resting for 10 seconds between lengths. Odd lengths, build to max from easy. Even lengths, tread water in deep end, then sprint to halfway, then easy. 200 metres easy catch-up with fins.<br><br>**Main set:** 2x400 metres with 1 minute rest between each 400 metres. Swim as 300 metres at 65%, 100 at 80%. First 400 metres with paddles, second 400 metres without. |
| **7** | **Subset:** 400 metres as 4 blocks of 1L easy then 2L build to 80%.<br><br>**Main set:** Swim as far as possible in 20 minutes. | **Subset:** 12x1L front crawl, resting for 15 seconds between lengths. Swim as alternate lengths of pull and kick with board. 200 metres easy alternate lengths of backstroke and breaststroke.<br><br>**Main set:** 100 metres with paddles and pull buoy at 60%, 100 metres with paddles and pull buoy at 80%. 45 seconds rest. 100 metres with fins at 50%, 100 metres with fins at 90%. 45 seconds rest. 100 metres with paddles and pull buoy at 60%, 100 metres with paddles and pull buoy at 80%. 45 seconds rest. 100 metres with fins at 50%, 100 metres with fins at 90%. 45 seconds rest. 100 metres with pull buoy at 60%, 100 metres with pull buoy at 80%. |
| **8** | **Subset:** 400 metres swum as four blocks of 2L front crawl, 1L front crawl kick. 200 metres easy alternate backstroke and breaststroke.<br><br>**Main set:** 400 metres front crawl, then rest for 1 minute. Build from first 100 metres at 60% to fourth 100 metres at 80%. 400 metres front crawl, then rest for 1 minute. Swim as 200 metres at 60%, then 200 metres with fins at 80%. 400 metres front crawl as 1L easy, 1L medium, 1L fast and repeated 4 times. Rest for 1 minute. 400 metres front crawl, then rest for 1 minute. Swim as 200 metres at 60%, then 200 metres with fins at 80%. | **Subset:** 400 metres swum as 4 blocks of 3L. Swim as 1L backstroke, 1L breaststroke, 1L front crawl build from 70% to 90%. 200 metres kick with fins and float.<br><br>**Main set:** 400 metres front crawl at 50%, then rest for 20 seconds. 300 metres front crawl with pull buoy at 60%, then rest for 30 seconds. 200 metres front crawl with paddles at 70%, then rest for 40 seconds. 100 metres front crawl with fins at 80%. |

# Key swimming terms

### ■ Arm cycle
The movement involved in completing the full arm action of a stroke.

### ■ Backstroke
A stroke where swimmers are on their back performing a **flutter kick** and rotating the arms alternately backwards.

### ■ Bilateral breathing
Breathing on alternate sides, usually either every third, fifth or seventh stroke.

### ■ Block
A period of work completed without rest as part of an **interval** session. Twelve **lengths**, for example, could be swum in four blocks of three lengths. The first length is swum at 60 per cent, the second at 70 per cent and the third at 80 per cent.

### ■ Breaststroke
A stroke where swimmers are on their front with their hands moving forwards then outwards while the legs **kick** in a frog-like motion.

### ■ Broken swim
Training method where you try to beat your best time for a distance by breaking it into smaller sections with short periods of rest. A 100-metre broken swim could be four 25-metre **lengths** swum at a pace that's faster than a quarter of your 100-metre time with five seconds rest between lengths.

### ■ Build
An increase in speed during a section of a pool workout. For example, 3x200 build would be a session where you swim the first 200 metres at, say, 60 per cent of your maximum pace, the second at 70 per cent and the third at 80 per cent.

### ■ Catch
The point in a stroke where the hand begins to propel the body forwards.

### ■ Catch-up
**Front crawl drill** where the swimmer completes one full **arm cycle** before starting the arm cycle on the opposite side.

### ■ Descend
To swim parts of a set progressively faster. Similar to **build** swims, but where you focus on time rather than on effort.

### ■ Drag
The natural resistance created by an object as it travels through the water. Drag cannot be eliminated entirely but can be reduced with an efficient stroke.

### ■ Drill
An exercise, such as **catch-up**, involving a specific part of a stroke and aimed at improving technique.

### ■ Fins
Training aid attached to the feet to assist movement through the water.

### ■ Flutter kick
A **kick**, performed in **front crawl** and **backstroke**, where the legs are straight and movement comes from the hips rather than from the knees.

### ■ Front crawl
The most common swimming stroke. Swimmers are on their front and perform a **flutter kick** with a forward motion of the arms.

### ■ Interval training
Repetitions of high-intensity activity separated by brief rest periods. Used as a way of increasing the amount of high-intensity work that you are able to perform in a session than if you did a continuous swim.

### ■ Kick
The leg movement a swimmer makes during a stroke.

### ■ Kick board
A training aid that you use with your arms extended in front of you. Used during **drills** that involve the legs only.

### ■ Length
The distance from one end of the pool to the other.

### ■ Main set
The central, often longest and most challenging, part of a swimming session. Should be constructed around a particular technique or fitness aim.

### ■ Negative split
Swim where the second half of a distance is completed in a faster time than the first.

### ■ Paddles
Discs (usually made from plastic) worn on the hands and used in **drills** to increase the surface area, and therefore resistance, being pulled through the water.

### ■ Pull
Swimming with only the arm movement, rather than the leg and arm movement, of a stroke.

### ■ Pull buoy
A floatation tool used in **drills**, which fits between a swimmer's legs to hold the feet up during drills that focus on the **arm cycle**.

### ■ Streamline
Body position that allows a swimmer to travel efficiently through the water. Used at the beginning of a **length** after pushing off from the wall.

### ■ Subset
Warm-up set before the **main set** of a training session. Used to practice **drills** and to prepare a swimmer for the physical demands of the main set.

### ■ Tumble turn
An underwater somersault that allows the swimmer to finish one **length** and begin another by pushing off from the wall with their feet without stopping.

# part 4

# Nutrition

Eat right to fuel your exercise with expert advice and a complete meal plan

# Six golden rules of eating for energy

## Eat according to these simple rules to complement your training

**1 Fuel your exercise**
To exercise efficiently, you need energy. That means eating the right food at the right time. Energy is created from the breakdown of carbohydrate, fat, protein and alcohol. When you eat a meal or have a drink, these components are broken down in the digestive system and released as a form of energy known as kilocalories.

The key to eating so that you have the energy to exercise is to eat a wide variety of foods that meet your carbohydrate, protein and fat needs. This should include plenty of fruit and vegetables to ensure an adequate supply of vitamins, minerals and fibre.

**2 Get the balance right**
No single food can provide all the essential nutrients, so having a balanced diet of carbohydrate, protein and fat is essential. Carbohydrates form the foundation of a healthy diet and are vital for giving you energy. They should make up about 60 per cent of your calorie intake, providing fuel in the form of glycogen.

Protein is associated with strength, making up part of the structure of every cell and tissue in your body. It is also needed for the growth and formation of new tissue and tissue repair, as well as being a fuel for energy. All proteins are made from building blocks called amino acids. There are 20 proteins in total, nine of which are considered to be essential because the body is unable to produce them itself. Good sources of complete protein are eggs, meat, fish, soya and dairy. Fat should make up 20 per cent of your total calorie intake. It's an important source

**Eat a balanced diet of carbs, protein and good fats**

of energy and provides essential fatty acids and the fat-soluble vitamins, A, D, E and K. Good fats are found in oily fish, olive oil and nuts.

### 3 Eat the right stuff

The simplest rule when deciding what to eat is to keep it as natural as possible − if you can't pronounce the ingredients on the label then don't eat it. Processed foods, such as cakes, pies and ready meals tend to be high in calories, full of added ingredients and low on essential nutrients. In short, they are poor at fuelling exercise and giving you sustained energy, but good at making you gain weight and sapping vital energy stores.

Include a wide variety of simple, unprocessed food in your diet

Carbohydrates come in many different forms and conventional advice suggests that we avoid simple carbohydrates. These are the sugars of the carbohydrate family and the ones that raise your blood sugar levels and encourage your body to store fat. Instead you should make sure that the majority of your carbs are unrefined, fall low on the glycaemic index (GI) and are high in fibre. These include wholemeal bread and pasta, oats, beans, fruits and vegetables, which release energy slowly and regulate your blood-sugar levels, ensuring you always have enough stored glycogen in your muscles to fuel an exercise session.

Protein-rich foods such as eggs, dairy and lean meat will ensure that you get the full range of amino acids. If you don't eat enough of these, you could lose lean muscle, which is needed for strength and speed. So, always make sure you eat a variety of protein-rich foods, but avoid it in the form of fatty meats and too much dairy, which can cause weight gain.

Fats come in four forms: saturates, found in meat and dairy products, monounsaturates, found in olive oil, nuts and seeds, polyunsaturates, found in vegetable oils and oily fish, and trans fats, which are produced by hydrogenating oils to make a solid fat often used in margarine, cakes and

pastries. The simple rule here is to keep saturates and trans fats to an absolute minimum, as they can increase the risk of high cholesterol and heart disease, and stock up on monounsaturated and polyunsaturated fats, especially the omega 3 and 6 varieties that our body cannot produce. Omega 3 fats, as found in oily fish have been proven to aid strength and endurance and protect joints from strains and inflammation.

### 4 More water

Exercise that causes you to sweat depletes your body of water quickly, so you should replace lost fluid as soon as possible. The trick is to make sure you are well hydrated before you start exercising and to drink plenty during and after exercise. Dehydration can have a huge impact on your performance, resulting in you feeling sluggish, fatigued, light headed and nauseous. Research suggests that a two per cent loss of fluid can result in a 20 per cent drop in

**Avoid dehydration by drinking water straight after exercise**

energy levels. Take a bottle out with you when exercising for long periods and aim to drink around 150ml every 15-20 minutes.

### 5 The supplement question

Supplements shouldn't be seen as an alternative to a good diet. Their purpose is to enhance performance, provide you with essential nutrients and speed recovery.

Sports drinks, such as isotonic drinks, are designed to deliver glucose to the muscles quickly, giving them extra energy.

A number of studies have shown that many sportspeople do not get an adequate intake of vitamins and minerals from their diet, so they will often need to get extra vitamins in the form of a multivitamin. Antioxidants are beneficial supplements, helping to mop up harmful free radicals caused by intense exercise and stress. You can also take an iron supplement, which can help prevent you from feeling fatigued and run down.

### 6 Time your meals

Ideally, you should eat at least two hours before exercise, leaving enough time for your food to digest. Aim to eat a low-GI meal based around wholemeal bread or wholegrain cereals, which will supply you with the sustained energy needed for exercise.

It is also vital to eat as soon as you can after your workout. During the first two hours after exercise, replenishment is most rapid, so eating high-GI carbohydrates with a source of quality protein during this time speeds up glycogen recovery and helps your body to prepare and recuperate for its next session. Try and have a white bagel filled with chicken or cottage cheese, or a yogurt and some fresh fruit.

# Energy meals

This plan contains the kind of foods you should be eating every day to fuel your exercise

## Monday

**Breakfast**
- 150g pot of low-fat yogurt. Sliced banana. 50g bran flakes.
- Glass of orange juice.

**Snack**
- 1 apple. 6 almonds.

**Lunch**
- Can of tuna served with salad and 140g brown rice.

**Snack**
- 2 sticks celery and oatcakes. 50g low fat cottage cheese. 200g berries.

**Dinner**
- Chicken fajitas: stir-fry 200g of chicken with a tbsp of olive oil. Mix 2 chopped tomatoes, a chopped onion, chilli and a tbsp of lemon juice. Serve with 3 wholemeal flour wraps and a glass of red wine.
- Tinned peaches in natural juice and 1 pot of plain yogurt.

**Snack**
- 40g Green & Black's Dark 70% organic chocolate.

**Daily total:**
- Calories 2,314

## Tuesday

**Breakfast**
- 45g porridge oats made with skimmed milk and a handful of berries. 2 slices wholemeal toast with low-fat spread.
- Glass of orange juice.

**Snack**
- Apple and 2tbsp organic peanut butter.

**Lunch**
- Tuna sandwich on 2 slices of wholemeal bread.
- Müllerlight yogurt.

**Snack**
- Handful of mixed nuts and raisins. 1 banana.

**Dinner**
- 200g chicken and vegetable stir-fry with sesame seeds and extra virgin olive oil. Serve with 70g brown rice.
- Pancakes with 150g blueberries.

**Snack**
- Strawberry and banana smoothie. Blend with ice cubes and 120g low-fat yogurt.

**Daily total:**
- Calories 2,099

## Wednesday

**Breakfast**
- 2 slices wholemeal toast with 2tsp peanut butter. 1 banana.
- Glass of apple juice.
- Mug of green tea.

**Snack**
- 5 dried apricots, cereal bar.
- Glass of skimmed milk.

**Lunch**
- Jacket potato with 1 small can of baked beans and 2tbsp grated low fat cheese.
- 2 satsumas and 1 apple.

**Snack**
- 120g low-fat yogurt with 50g blueberries and a handful of jumbo oats.

**Dinner**
- 225g lean steak, served with 5 new potatoes, broccoli and spinach.
- Bowl of homemade fruit salad.

**Snack**
- 40g Green & Black's Dark 70% organic chocolate.

**Daily total:**
- Calories 2,085

## Thursday

**Breakfast**
☐ 45g Special K cereal, served with 5 chopped strawberries, low-fat yogurt and a handful of flaked almonds.

**Snack**
☐ 50g whey protein smoothie, with 300ml skimmed milk and 50g blueberries.

**Lunch**
☐ Carton of New Covent Garden carrot and coriander soup, 1 wholemeal roll and 1 apple.

**Snack**
☐ 1 mashed banana on 2 slices of wholemeal bread, with 1 tbsp peanut butter.

**Dinner**
☐ 100g lean minced turkey with tomato sauce and 1 chopped onion. 70g wholemeal spaghetti.
☐ 150g low fat yogurt and 200g berries.

**Snack**
☐ 1 cereal bar, 1 apple and 5 strawberries.

**Daily total:**
☐ Calories 2,259

## Friday

**Breakfast**
☐ Mug of green tea.
☐ Handful of raw oats with 200ml skimmed milk and 1tsp honey, 1 grapefruit.

**Snack**
☐ Handful of mixed nuts and raisins, 2 apples.

**Lunch**
☐ 50g wholemeal pasta with 1 chicken breast in chunky vegetable pasta sauce.
☐ Small shop-bought smoothie.

**Snack**
☐ 1 pear and 2tbsp peanut butter.

**Dinner**
☐ 85g pasta with 185g can of tuna. Mix in ½ finely-chopped red pepper, 10 roughly-chopped cherry tomatoes and fresh-ground black pepper.
☐ 1 small glass of red wine.

**Snack**
☐ 150g pot of plain yoghurt and 50g strawberries.

**Daily total:**
☐ Calories 2,154

## Saturday

**Breakfast**
☐ 2 scrambled eggs on 2 slices of wholemeal toast.
☐ 1 grapefruit.

**Snack**
☐ 20g whey protein smoothie made with 300ml skimmed milk, 50g raspberries and a handful of goji berries.

**Lunch**
☐ Large sweet potato with 1 small can of baked beans and 2tbsp grated low-fat cheese.
☐ 1 low fat yogurt.

**Snack**
☐ Pear and 2tbsp peanut butter.

**Dinner**
☐ 200g baked cod, 5 new potatoes, broccoli and green beans.
☐ 2 oranges.

**Snack**
☐ 500ml skimmed chocolate milk blended with 2 bananas, 2 teaspoons whey protein powder and 6 ice cubes.

**Daily total:**
☐ Calories 2,070

## Sunday

**Breakfast**
☐ 2 poached eggs, 2 slices of wholemeal toast and a glass of orange juice.

**Snack**
☐ 2 oatcakes with low-fat cream cheese and apple.

**Lunch**
☐ 125g roast pork, 100g roast potatoes and 200g roasted root vegetables, 50ml Bisto gravy.
☐ Slice of apple pie.

**Snack**
☐ 120g low-fat yogurt with 50g blueberries and blackberries.

**Dinner**
☐ 130g oven-baked salmon steak. 1 sweet potato. 1tbsp low-fat coleslaw. 75g garden peas.
☐ 1 chopped pear and low-fat yogurt.

**Snack**
☐ Handful of nuts and dried fruit.

**Daily total:**
☐ Calories 2,214

Thanks to Matt Punsheon at Lifetime Training (lifetimehf.co.uk) and Neil ODell at Premier Training International (premierglobal.co.uk)

# Eat for victory

Prepare better and recover quicker with this pre- and post-exercise nutrition guide

### Pre-race nutrition
The food you eat before a race should satisfy your hunger and keep your muscles, blood and liver topped up with glucose throughout the event. Your body needs carbohydrate-rich foods with a moderate to high glycaemic index (GI) value. This will provide a quick source of carbohydrate and glycogen (short-term energy). Good foods to eat are jacket potatoes, white pasta with tomato sauce, and toast with jam. The following advice applies whether you're doing a standard exercise session or a race.

### What to eat before a short race
There is no need to carb load before a short race, but you will need to eat in order to top up your liver's glycogen stores and help maintain your blood sugar levels. Plan to have your main pre-competition meal two hours before the event. This will allow enough time for your food to settle. The meal itself should be based around moderate-GI carbohydrates, such as a bowl of muesli, which is low in fat and not too bulky or filling.

### Mid-exercise eating
When exercising for longer than an hour, keep your blood sugar and energy levels topped up by drinking an isotonic sports drink, taking energy gels (half a sachet, with a cup of water) or eating high-GI snacks, such as jelly beans or bananas.

Begin consuming these about 30 minutes after you start exercising and continue to eat them at regular intervals to help maintain your performance.

If you're racing for less than 60 minutes, water is all you need to counteract dehydration. Aim to drink about 250ml every 20 minutes.

### What to eat before a long race
On race day your main objectives are to top up liver glycogen stores, maintain your blood sugar levels before and during the race, and stay hydrated.

Eat breakfast two to three hours before the race and go for slow-release (low-GI) carbohydrates, such as porridge with raisins and honey, with a little protein, such as low-fat milk or yoghurt. Most importantly, you should stick with familiar foods that you find easy to digest. You also need to make sure you drink enough water to keep yourself hydrated.

**Pre-race meal**
**Pasta with tomato sauce**
Never skip your evening meal if you're racing the next day. Stick to high-carbohydrate foods with a moderate to low fibre content and avoid alcohol because it's a diuretic. A bowl of white pasta with a tomato-based sauce is the perfect pre-race meal. The pasta will help to keep glycogen stores at their maximum while the tomato sauce is full of vitamins and antioxidants to help keep you alert the next day.

### Post-race nutrition
After racing, your body needs to do two things: firstly rehydrate and secondly replace the carbohydrate that was stored in your muscles and has been used up during exercise. Your aim is to re-stock your glycogen stores and repair damaged muscle fibres as soon as possible. Your body will need foods with a high-GI rating for an immediate energy boost, such as an energy bar or a Jaffa Cake. As for fluids, you'll need to drink at least 500ml of fluid and continue drinking regularly throughout the day.

### What to eat after a short race
You need to refuel within 20 minutes after the race. Try to have a snack that contains 20-40g of protein, such as a yogurt, and 60-120g of carbohydrates, such as a bowl of wholegrain cereal. Eating carbohydrates immediately after strenuous exercise will encourage recovery and take advantage of the enhanced rate of glycogen storage. The protein will help your muscles repair and also help restock glycogen stores.

### What to eat after a long race
Eat carb-heavy food within 15 minutes of finishing the race. This will help you to make the most of the 'window of opportunity' − the time that your body has an enhanced ability to utilize such nutrients as carbohydrate and protein. You should also try to eat a combination of carbs and protein. This blend stimulates insulin release, which prompts your muscles to absorb glucose and amino acids from the bloodstream. You may not feel like eating straight after a long race, but a peanut butter sandwich followed by a banana is a good start.

**Post-race meal**
**Jacket potato with cheese and beans**
Choose foods with a moderate to high GI rating to ensure rapid refuelling. Try to avoid going for rich meals as these will delay the recovery process and make you feel bloated.

A jacket potato with cheese and beans has the high-GI carbs that will get into your bloodstream and muscle cells fast, and the protein to help repair muscle fibres, all without containing too much fat. The beans will also provide you with antioxidants to speed up recovery, and lots of fibre to stop you getting hungry again too quickly.

# Nuggets of advice

## These instant food fixes will add extra fuel to your exercise

### Don't run on empty
Don't believe that training on an empty stomach burns more fat. It can in fact have a negative impact on your performance. Studies have shown that performance improves when you train after eating a moderately high-carbohydrate, low-fat meal such as a jacket potato with either cottage cheese or beans. Eat this about three hours before exercise to avoid a stitch and a heavy stomach.

### Avoid quick-fix foods
If you need food fast then don't turn to fast foods and soft drinks. They are full of energy-sapping sugar, saturated fat and salt, which won't fill you up or satisfy your appetite. Instead, have a homemade milkshake using fresh fruit and yogurt, a bowl of wholegrain cereal or a handful of dried fruit and nuts.

### Rehydrate with milk
Water and sports drinks aren't the only re-hydration options. Drinking a glass of skimmed milk after exercise is just as effective as isotonic drinks at revitalising the body. Recent research has shown that milk also provides an excellent source of natural energy, protein and vitamins and minerals.

### Grab an orange
Eat oranges regularly and you may experience less muscle soreness after hard exercise sessions. A study

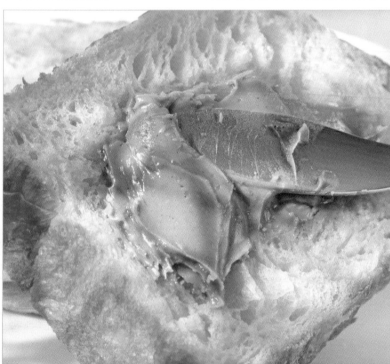

### Slap on the peanut butter
Peanut butter is a great food for athletes. It is packed with protein, fibre, healthy fats, iron, calcium and B vitamins. It can even help lower blood cholesterol levels, which can help you control your weight. Not bad for a humble sandwich spread, eh?

### Carry some raisins
The shrivelled fruits can give you an important energy boost. *The Journal of Strength and Conditioning Research* says they are as effective as sports gels in boosting energy ahead of short-term exercise.

### Have a banana
You can lose up to 200mg of potassium per hour when exercising, which can cause cramps and weakness. Replace lost the minerals with a banana, which contains about 422mg of potassium. As well as giving you a potassium fix, they are also a natural source of energy.

by the University of North Carolina at Greensboro showed that taking vitamin C supplements for two weeks prior to challenging exercise helped alleviate post-exercise muscle soreness.

### Weigh yourself
Step on the scales before and after running to calculate how much weight you have lost during exercise then drink with the aim of bringing your weight back up to it's pre-exercise level. Replacing lost fluids as quickly as possible after running will speed up your recovery and will curb hunger pangs.

### Stick to what you know
Play it safe pre-race and only eat the same type of food that you have used during training. Taking part in a race while fuelled by unfamiliar foods could give you an upset stomach.

### Look in the loo
Passing dark yellow urine is a sign that you're dehydrated. If you're doing an early morning run or cycle then drink water the night before and have another glass first thing in the morning. To ensure proper hydration, take a water bottle out with you and sip regularly.

### Stock up on carbs
Increase your carb intake in the days before a longer race to maximize your glycogen stores (your fuel resource for exercise). Indulge in carb-dense foods such as pasta, peanut butter on wholemeal toast, porridge and rice.

### Make your own sports drink
Isotonic drinks have the same concentration of sugar and salts as the blood. That means they are absorbed rapidly, providing a speedy delivery of energy and hydration − perfect for a session lasting more than one hour. Make your own by mixing 200ml of ordinary fruit squash, 800ml water and a pinch of salt.

### Have a coffee
You might think that it's wise to steer clear of coffee before a run but, in fact, drinking a cup can give you a boost, particularly before a short run. You may however find that you need a toilet stop so have a small cup and avoid milky drinks such as a cappuccino because they're harder to digest.

### Avoid sporty spice
Try not to eat spicy food before a race or the night before a long race. Moderate exercise stimulates muscle contraction of the colon, which speeds up the rate of bowel movement. Spicy foods can accelerate that process even further, resulting in an urgent toilet stop.

### Refuel your muscles
Top up your glycogen stores with carb-heavy foods such as pasta and serve them with a portion of protein such as chicken, beans or eggs. One study at the University of Texas found that meals with a ratio of three parts carbohydrate to one part protein boosted glycogen storage by almost 40 per cent.

# part 5

# Triathlon

Use your new skills and sport-specific
training advice to take on a triathlon

# Three become one

## It's everything you've just read about, but together in one race

In Hawaii in 1977 an argument broke out between members of a running club and a swimming club over who were the fittest athletes: runners or swimmers. Then a US Navy Commander, John Collins, pointed out that Belgian cyclist Eddy Merckx had the highest recorded maximum oxygen uptake of any athlete ever measured, and that perhaps cyclists were the fittest athletes of all.

There was only one way to find out: a race involving all three disciplines. This is how the world-famous Hawaii Ironman event was born, and how triathlon gained global attention.

### What is triathlon?
A triathlon is simply a race that includes swimming, cycling and running, done back-to-back with the time taken in transition (moving from one discipline to the next) included in the overall time of the race. The distance of a triathlon is not set but there are a few standard distances – which are outlined below – that have become the norm.

### Who is triathlon for?
Triathlon is among the fastest growing sports in the UK. You do have to have a decent level of fitness to take part in a race, but you don't have to be a super-human athlete. Major events such as the London Triathlon (Olympic distance) now attract tens of

thousands of competitors, all looking to challenge themselves in what is being seen as the ultimate test of all-round cardiovascular fitness.

Triathlon appeals to people who are looking for a challenge beyond their usual running or cycling routines, and the plethora of exciting equipment required to take part in triathlon is a great incentive to gear heads who can't be seen without the latest carbon-frame bike. At the very least, to enter a triathlon you will need a wetsuit, goggles, a decent bike and some good running shoes. But when the triathlon bug takes hold there is no limit to the amount of go-faster kit you can buy to feed your new obsession.

This section will tell you everything you need to know about getting started in triathlon: training, races, tips, transitions and gear. If your normal sessions in the gym are feeling a bit dull, triathlon offers the motivation you need to take your fitness to new levels.

## Triathlon distances

|  | ■ Swim | ■ Bike | ■ Run |
|---|---|---|---|
| Super sprint | 400m | 10km | 2.5km |
| Sprint | 750m | 20km | 5km |
| Olympic | 1,500m | 40km | 10km |
| Full (Ironman) | 3.8km | 180km | 42.2km |

It should be noted that Ironman is the brand name of a particular series of events, but it has also become synonymous with the gruelling, long-distance race that includes a full marathon for the running leg.

# Tri it on

## Cool gear is one of the best bits about triathlon. Here's what you need

### Wetsuit

If you're taking part in a UK race that involves an open water swim, you'll need a wetsuit. Not just because they prevent you from freezing, but because they're compulsory. Get a special triathlon suit, which will be designed not to chafe, to allow maximum freedom of movement at the shoulders and, handily, to make you more buoyant.

**Pictured: Blueseventy Synergie wetsuit, £270.**

### Footware

■ **Cycling shoes**
You can wear regular cycling shoes but a triathlon-specific pair will save you time in transition. Single Velcro strap shoes are quicker to get on and off than those with three straps. A seamless, quick-drying lining means you won't get blisters if you don't wear them with socks.
**Pictured: Shimano TR50 Triathlon Shoe, £109.99.**

■ **Running shoes**
You can wear regular road running shoes but you'll lose time tying the laces. Make your shoes triathlon friendly by using elastic laces. If you're really serious about racing, get a triathlon pair. Zoot trainers, for example, have elastic laces, friction-free lining so you don't have to wear socks and a drainage system that lets water out through the base. The extra support at the midsole takes into account the different running style triathletes adopt when they've just come off a bike.
**Pictured: Zoot Ultra TT, £90.**

## Tri-suit

You may not reach for one of these all-in-ones for sartorial reasons but wearing a tri-suit will save you time during a race. They're lightweight and fast-drying and fit under your wetsuit, which is vital when you don't have time for costume changes. The panelling is stitched and contoured to work with the way your body moves and will help prevent chafing.

**Pictured: Orca Perform tri-suit, £99.**

## Goggles

It's important to know where you're going in open water swimming if you want to avoid veering off course and increasing the distance you have to swim. Some triathletes favour mask-style goggles (such as the ones below), which increase your range of vision. Go for an anti-fogging pair with tinted lenses that will help you see in the sun. Other racers prefer to use standard swimming goggles but whatever you buy, the most important thing is that they're comfortable to wear.

**Pictured: Aquasphere Vista goggles, £18.99.**

## Tri accessories

### Extra gear to give you an edge

### ■ Training watch

Keep tabs on your performance with a water resistant heart rate monitor. Getting one with a speed and distance function will give you even more feedback on how your training is going. Most allow you to store training sessions and programme interval sessions.

**Pictured: Timex Ironman Bodylink, £184.99.**

### ■ Tri bag

You'll need a good sports bag to carry all your triathlon kit. Get one with plenty of room and a number of different compartments, including a dry storage one for your wetsuit and post-race or training kit.

**Pictured: Orca sports bag, £45.**

### ■ Sunglasses

Sunnies aren't just for posers. It's important to get a pair that protects your eyes from dirt and the Sun and gives a good range of vision. You also need to know that they'll stay in place because repositioning them will slow you down.

**Pictured: Oakley Radar, £119.99.**

# Anatomy of a triathlon bike

## Bikes are the kings of triathlon kit. This is what the top models offer

You can use a standard road bike for a triathlon but getting into the sport gives you a great excuse to buy a shiny new bike. Triathlon bikes are similar to time trial bikes, in that they're designed with a narrow profile so they get the rider through the air with the least resistance possible. Triathletes don't usually draft, so your bike needs to be aerodynamic. That's why the riding position is often low with the rider almost tucked up to create a smaller wind profile. To maximise aerodynamics, triathlon bikes are often fitted with tri-bars (also known as aerobars), which jut out at the front and allow the rider to tuck their elbows into their sides. This position makes it easier to flow through the air although it does make it more difficult to steer the bike.

### ■ Seat post
The seat post on a triathlon bike can be more vertical than on an average road bike to give a riding position that is further forward and take strain off the hamstrings.

### ■ Disk wheel
Found on expensive top-level bikes, disk wheels can significantly reduce wheel drag. They are heavier than spoked wheels though, so are best suited to flat courses. They are also not suited to riding in crosswinds.

### ■ Gears
Close gear ratios are for flat courses. If you're taking part in a hilly race, you'll need to swap the cassette for one with bigger sprockets.

■ **Frame**

An oval, rather than round, cross-section tubing can be used in the frame and fork to smooth airflow over the bike. Most triathlon bike courses are flat so aerodynamics becomes more important and weight becomes slightly less important.

■ **Wheels**

Some triathlon bikes have slightly smaller wheels than the average road bike. This gives them a smaller cross section area, which reduces wind resistance.

■ **Tri-bars**

The special handlebars are designed to promote an aerodynamic riding position. The centrally positioned handgrips allow the rider to tuck their arms into their body.

■ **Wheel rim**

A deep-section wheel rim will improve aerodynamics because it promotes airflow over the wheel.

**Tri bike tip**

Attach two water bottles to your frame for longer races because the bike is the best time to refuel during a race. Fill one bottle with water and the other with an energy drink.

■ **Spokes**

Fewer spokes make the wheel more aerodynamic. Flat spokes add an extra level of aerodynamics.

**Main image:** Felt DA 2008 Triathlon Bike, £4,499.99.

# The fourth discipline

## Get your best race time with the right preparation and smooth transitions

### Before the race

**Sort everything the night before**
That means checking your bike, pumping up tyres, sticking race numbers to your kit, taping energy gels to your bike frame – anything that will save you having to waste time on race day.

**Get there early**
You'll perform better if you are in a calm state of mind, so don't find yourself rushing to get to the start line because you couldn't find a parking space at the venue.

**Put your bike in gear**
Think about what gear you want to start the race in. Too low or high and you won't manage a quick getaway.

**Clip your shoes onto your pedals**
Bike shoes can be treacherous to run in, so it's much easier to keep them clipped into your pedals while you run through the transition area to the mounting-up zone. Then you can get onto your bike and pedal with your feet resting on top of your shoes for the first few metres, and slip your feet into your shoes once you are under way. This is something you should practise frequently before the race.

**Personalise your transition position**
On race day there will be lots of people with similar-looking kit. If you want to be able to find yours in the crowd, mark it with something easy to spot, such as a bright towel.

**Keep food and drink easily accessible**
Have an energy drink ready in transition for a quick refuel. Tape energy gels to your bike frame and have a disposable bottle of water ready for the start of the run. Drink it as you leave the transition and chuck it when it's empty.

**Walk through transitions beforehand and look for landmarks**
When you come out of the swim you will be tired and disoriented. Make sure you know the route from the end of the swim to your bike well, so you don't get lost. It's worth noting permanent landmarks near to your position because knowing yours is the fifth bike in the line won't help if the other bikes aren't there when you arrive.

**Suit up early**
Put your wetsuit on a good ten to 15 minutes before the race starts. This will give it time to warm up and make it more flexible when you start the swim.

**Place your swim cap over your goggle strap**
Then if your goggles get knocked off in the race you won't lose them altogether.

**Pick your place in the swim pack**
If you're not a strong swimmer, you don't want to be at the front of the group when the hooter goes. The pack will just swim over the top of you. Pick a spot to the side or middle of the group. Not at the back – that's just defeatist.

**Racers prepare for action at the London Triathlon**

## T1 First transition: swim to bike

### Don't remove your goggles
As you exit the water lift your goggles but don't take them off. This leaves your hands free to work at getting your wetsuit off.

### Unzip as you run
As you run into transition, unzip your wetsuit and pull it down over your shoulders. By the time you get to your bike you should have the wetsuit pulled down to your waist.

### Lube up
Getting a wet wetsuit over hands and feet can be tricky, but there are lubricants that can help to slip it off more easily. Rub them on your wrists and ankles before the race. Don't use Vaseline as it can damage the material on some wetsuits.

### Cut it down
It may seem insane to take scissors to an expensive wetsuit, but some people cut the ends off the arms and legs to make the suit easier to remove.

### Stay standing
Roll your wetsuit as far down your legs as you can, then stand on it to pull your legs free. Try to avoid sitting down to remove your wetsuit as this is more tiring and time consuming.

### Don't forget the goggles
Only once the wetsuit is off should you remove your cap and goggles.

### Helmet on first
Most races will oblige you to put your helmet on before you touch your bike. Get used to this and practise before.

### Know where to mount up
Run with your bike through the transition area and be sure to only mount up when you are in the mounting zone. You will be penalised otherwise.

### Do a flying mount
You might want to practise this beforehand, but if you can mount your bike with a running leap you can get the jump on others who stop to mount their bike.

### Pedal with your feet on your shoes
Place your feet on top of your shoes (which should already be clipped into the pedals) and pedal until you have a good rhythm going before slipping your feet into your shoes.

# **T2** Second transition: bike to run

### Fuel up before the run
The bike is the best place to take on fluids and gels to keep energy levels high. About 20 minutes before you reach the end of the bike leg, take on some fuel for the run. If you wait until you're in transition to glug down a gel, it won't take effect in time.

### Stretch your legs as you near T2
In the final few hundred metres of the bike leg, stand up in the pedals and stretch out your calves and hamstrings as you cycle. This will help to prepare your legs for the sudden change in physical stresses when you start running.

### Unfasten your shoes
As you approach the dismount area, unfasten your shoes and slip your heels out. You should still be able to cycle into the jump-off zone and, as soon as you're there, you can take your feet out ready for a quick dismount.

### Be sure to stop before the dismount line
If you're not concentrating and you go over the line you will be penalised or made to back up and make your approach again.

### Run in bare feet
It's a lot faster than slipping around in bike shoes.

### Find your place
Remember, your position in transition will look different because the other bikes will have moved. And be careful when racking your bike – it can be easy in your haste to knock over other people's bikes, which won't make you very popular.

### Rack bike, helmet off
Remember that order. If you remove your helmet first you could be disqualified from the race.

### Running shoes on
Are you a socks or no-socks person? No socks will save you time in transition, but it's not worth it if you get blisters during the run. Only run without socks if you are certain that you will be blister free.

### Go elastic
Replacing your normal laces with elastic ones can shave a few seconds off your transition time. Get elastic laces with a pull-lock system and be sure to test them thoroughly before race day.

### Less haste, more speed
In general, the best way to be sure of a good transition time is to think clearly, be calm and don't be rushed, even if you're keen to get the jump on your rivals. A poorly-executed transition will only lose you time in the long run, either because you forget to pick something up (it's not unheard of for competitors to grab the wrong bike in their hurry to get through transition) or because something goes wrong, such as your feet starting to hurt because you didn't put your socks on properly.

### Practise
Transitions are the fourth discipline in triathlon and you should practise them regularly. A good transition can put you several places ahead of your rivals when the final times are announced.

# Power of three

## Get faster and stay injury free by including a strength and stability workout in your training regime

The bulk of your triathlon training should be spent swimming, cycling and running. But that doesn't mean you have to avoid the gym. Performing the following strength moves will give you explosive power during a race, which is important for bursts of speed and overtaking. The stability exercises will make you more efficient in each of the three disciplines and help reduce your risk of injury. Do the following moves in order, twice a week on non-swim, bike or run days to supplement your triathlon training and improve your performance.

### 1 Clean to squat
**Sets:** 3 **Reps:** 8

■ Bend your knees to grab the barbell with an unstressed lower back.
■ Drive up, lifting the bar and pushing your elbows out.
■ Drop down into a squat to catch the bar, then straighten up.

**Why do it?** This exercise fires every muscle in your body into motion, preparing you for the rest of the workout and maximising muscle fatigue by the end of the workout.

## 2 Medicine ball press-up

**Sets:** 3 **Reps:** 10

■ Start with your right hand on the ball, lower and press up.
■ Place both hands on the ball then move your right hand off to the right.
■ Lower, press up and go back the other way to complete one rep.
■ Don't arch your back or let your hips drop down.

**Why do it?** Introducing a lateral movement to the press up makes it harder, strengthening your chest for the swim and stabilising your shoulders.

## 3 Barbell calf raise

**Sets:** 3 **Reps:** 10

■ Keep looking ahead with your shoulder blades retracted.
■ Drop your heels off the box then rise up quickly.
■ Lower slowly for 4 seconds before exploding up again.
■ Keep your core braced throughout.

**Why do it?** By lowering your heels slowly, you're increasing the eccentric loading of the muscle. This strengthens the Achilles and other tendons to protect against injury.

## 4 Gym ball jackknife
**Sets: 3 Reps: 12**

■ Place your toes on top of the ball.
■ Set your shoulders and keep your core braced.
■ Slowly roll the ball to bring your knees into your chest.
■ Pause and contract your abs before rolling the ball back.

**Why do it?** Your abdominal muscles can deactivate during the bike leg, so this move redresses the balance by targeting the abs and core.

## 5 Side plank star
**Sets: 4 Reps: 5**

■ Start with your body in a straight line from neck to ankles.
■ Make sure your hips don't dip.
■ Lift your top arm and leg up at the same time.
■ Hold for 2-10 seconds and alternate sides with each set.

**Why do it?** Static holds are effective for core activation. This one is particularly good because it introduces instability when you lift your arm and leg in the air.

## 6 Wobble cushion one-leg squat

**Sets:** 3 **Reps:** 10 each side

■ Stand with one foot on the cushion, keeping your feet close together.
■ Lower by lifting up the non-working foot and bending your other knee.
■ Swap legs after ten reps.

**Why do it?** This move trains the chain of muscles that runs from your ankle all the way up your leg and into your core, maintaining their strength whichever way your ankle is turning.

## 7 Stork hold

**Sets:** 4 **Time:** 10-60 seconds

■ Start with your body relaxed and your feet hip-width apart.
■ Lean forward, lift your arms up and to the side, then lift one foot.
■ Slowly lift the rear leg up to work the other hamstring.
■ Hold this pose for as long as you can and swap sides after each set.

**Why do it?** This is popular with triathlon coaches because it teaches control and develops hamstring strength.

# Rise to the challenge

## Be at your best on race day with these timesaving tips

### Start with purpose
Start the swim as hard as you can without completely knackering yourself. That will prevent you from getting swum over by eager competitors and getting caught up in petty fights, which will waste energy. Once you're in a good position, you can find a sustainable rhythm.

### Get into a slipstream
During the swim, find someone who is slightly faster than you and get into their slipstream. If you swim behind their feet, they'll break up the water so there's less resistance to slow you down.

### Increase your stroke cadence
In open water, you want to maintain a fast stroke cadence to chop through the waves and keep your momentum.

### Point your toes to reduce drag
Pointing your toes away from your body will reduce drag when you're swimming in a wetsuit. Kick with your legs almost straight, using small up-and-down motions (rather than bending at the

### Comfort over weight
People can get obsessed with shaving 20g off their bike's weight in the belief that it will make them cycle faster. Ridding yourself of excess weight is a good idea, but it's more important to find a comfortable riding position that will allow you to channel your effort effectively.

knee or scissoring sideways) to support your body and avoid fatiguing your larger muscles, which you will need for the cycle and run.

### Know where you're going
Look up every six to eight strokes to make sure you're going in the right direction. Failing to take a direct line between the buoys means you'll have to swim further. Take a slightly wider route when going round buoys to avoid getting caught up in a group of swimmers.

### Kick to end the swim
Towards the end of the swim, kick your legs harder so that the blood flows through them and warms them up properly for the bike.

### Refuel on the bike
Carry water and energy drink on your bike and tape energy gels to the frame so you don't have to pick them up in transitions. Refuelling on the bike is better as it's easier than doing it on the run.

### Cut corners
When you're cornering on the bike, go in wide, cut in at the shortest line and come out wide. Lift up your inside knee and place your weight on your inside handlebar. Break before rather than in the corner to avoid crashing.

### End the bike stage easy...
Don't cycle too hard at the end of the bike stage (the last 5km if you're doing an Olympic distance triathlon), because your legs will be exhausted when you start the run.

### ...but speed up before transition
Put in a few extra pedal strokes to make sure you're at the front of your group when you come in for the second transition. You'll save yourself vital seconds by not getting caught up at the back of a bunch of riders. Do brick sessions running off the bike to make sure you can cope with the last-minute speed burst.

### Go short and fast
The most efficient way to run and pedal during a triathlon is to use short,

**Don't stop**
If you think you can't go on, don't stop. As soon as you stop, your body releases calming chemicals to start the recovery process. It's hard to carry on after that so, if you're struggling, slow your pace and control your breathing.

fast steps and cycles. Aim for 90-100 revolutions per minute on the bike. Conversely, make each swimming stroke as long as possible.

### Stretch to avoid cramp
Rehydrating on the bike can help you avoid getting cramp on the run. Stretching your calves towards the end of the bike will also help. Bend one heel to the road and place your weight on that leg.

### Find a pacemaker
If someone's running at a similar pace to you, slot in behind them and let them take some of the wind resistance off you. If you're trying to overtake, pick people off one by one to give you a series of achievable short-term goals.

### Break down the run
Break the run down into sections so it becomes more mentally manageable. If you're doing an Olympic-distance triathlon, have a strategy that splits the run into a beginning, where you get into a rhythm, a middle, where you hold your place or overtake if you can, and an end, where you put every last ounce of effort into finishing as strongly as you can.

### Disciplined transitions
Transitions are the fourth discipline in triathlon, so treat them as seriously as you would any other part of the race. Have a plan about how you're going to get through the transitions in the fastest possible time and try to stick to it.

# Get ready to race

Whatever your level, these race-distance plans will put you on track for success

I f you want to enter a triathlon, you must follow a structured plan. You have to train all three disciplines and get used to performing them back to back, so sessions need to be planned carefully. The trick is to train each discipline sufficiently, but also have enough time to recover. As a result, triathlon plans often involve several training days per week, so it's even more important to mark the sessions in your diary and keep a training log to monitor your progress.

The super sprint plan is aimed at first time triathletes. The objective is to get you into the habit of training regularly and get your body used to doing more than one discipline in the same session. The sprint plan builds up gradually to give you both stamina and speed and can be used by first timers, as well as more experienced racers. The Olympic plan is where you step up your training distances, completing a substantial volume of work each week to develop endurance.

### Effort level

Some sessions in the plans in this section use an effort level from 1 to 10 to tell you how hard you should be pushing yourself. Here's what the numbers mean.

**1-4** Easy up to a gentle pace
**5-6** Able to have a conversation
**6-7** Getting out of breath
**8-9** Can't talk, uncomfortable
**10** Flat-out sprint

# Super sprint plan

## You're only eight weeks away from becoming a triathlete

The super sprint race distance (400m swim, 10km bike, 2.5km run) is relatively short and that's reflected in the training sessions. This programme is aimed at novices. The important thing is to train consistently, building up speed and distance throughout the plan and getting used to brick sessions where you do two disciplines back to back. By week four you'll have completed the race distance for each of the three legs in individual sessions. Week six involves some higher-intensity work to give you a speed boost. You complete the longest distance sessions in the penultimate week before tapering your training to make sure you're fresh for race day.

| ■ Week 1 | ■ Week 2 | ■ Week 3 | ■ Week 4 | ■ Week 5 | ■ Week 6 | ■ Week 7 | ■ Week 8 |
|---|---|---|---|---|---|---|---|
| **Monday** Rest | **Monday** Rest | **Monday** Rest | **Monday** Rest | **Monday** Rest | **Monday** Rest | **Monday** Rest | **Monday** Rest |
| **Tuesday** Swim 300m | **Tuesday** Swim 300m | **Tuesday** Swim 350m | **Tuesday** Swim 350m | **Tuesday** Swim 400m | **Tuesday** Interval session: swim 10x50m at level 8-9, rest for 1 minute between reps | **Tuesday** Swim 500m | **Tuesday** Swim 300m |
| **Wednesday** Bike 6km | **Wednesday** Bike 6km | **Wednesday** Bike 8km | **Wednesday** Bike 8km | **Wednesday** Bike 10km | **Wednesday** Interval session: bike 5x2km at level 8, level 4 for 2 mins between reps | **Wednesday** Bike 12km | **Wednesday** Bike 6km |
| **Thursday** Run 3km | **Thursday** Run 3km | **Thursday** Run 4km | **Thursday** Run 4km | **Thursday** Run 5km | **Thursday** Rest | **Thursday** Run 6km | **Thursday** Run 3km |
| **Friday** Rest | **Friday** Rest | **Friday** Rest | **Friday** Swim 400m | **Friday** Bike 10km | **Friday** Run 5x1km at level 8, level 4 for 2 mins between reps | **Friday** Swim 500m | **Friday** Rest |
| **Saturday** Swim 300m | **Saturday** Bike 8km | **Saturday** Run 4km | **Saturday** Bike 10k | **Saturday** Run 5km | **Saturday** Swim 400m | **Saturday** Bike 10km | **Saturday** Rest |
| **Sunday** Brick session: bike 6km, run 3km without resting | **Sunday** Brick session: swim 300m, run 3km without resting | **Sunday** Brick session: swim 300m, bike 8km without resting | **Sunday** Brick session: bike 10km, run 3km without resting | **Sunday** Rest | **Sunday** Brick session: bike 10km, run 4km without resting | **Sunday** Brick session: bike 12km, run 4km without resting | **Sunday** Super sprint triathlon |

# Sprint plan

## This beginner-friendly 12-week plan combines speed and stamina

Sprint races (800m swim, 20km bike, 5km run) are a good introduction to triathlon. They're not so short that you feel under pressure to go flat out, but they're long enough to be a substantial challenge. This plan starts by getting you used to training several days a week before introducing brick sessions. Once you're comfortable with switching from one discipline to the other in the same session, you then up the distance of your sessions to improve stamina. The second half of the plan focuses on increasing intensity and on completing the race distance in each of the disciplines on consecutive days. In the final week you taper your training so you're fresh for race day.

| ■ Week 1 | ■ Week 2 | ■ Week 3 | ■ Week 3 | ■ Week 5 | ■ Week 6 |
|---|---|---|---|---|---|
| **Monday** Rest | **Monday** Rest | **Monday** Rest | **Monday** Rest | **Monday** Rest | **Monday** Rest |
| **Tuesday** Swim 400m | **Tuesday** Swim 500m | **Tuesday** Brick session: Bike 6km, run 3km without resting | **Tuesday** Brick session: Bike 8km, run 4km without resting | **Tuesday** Bike 15km | **Tuesday** Bike 15km |
| **Wednesday** Bike 6km | **Wednesday** Bike 8km | **Wednesday** Swim 600m | **Wednesday** Swim 600m | **Wednesday** Swim 600m | **Wednesday** Swim 600m |
| **Thursday** Run 3km | **Thursday** Run 4km | **Thursday** Brick session: swim 500m, bike 8km without resting | **Thursday** Brick session: swim 600m, bike 10km without resting | **Thursday** Run 8km | **Thursday** Run 8km |
| **Friday** Rest | **Friday** Rest | **Friday** Rest | **Friday** Rest | **Friday** Bike 25km | **Friday** Bike 25km |
| **Saturday** Swim 500m | **Saturday** Swim 600m | **Saturday** Run 5km | **Saturday** Run 5km | **Saturday** Swim 900m | **Saturday** Swim 900m |
| **Sunday** Bike 8km | **Sunday** Run 5km | **Sunday** Bike 15km | **Sunday** Bike 15km | **Sunday** Brick session: bike 8km, run 4km without resting | **Sunday** Brick session: bike 8km, run 4km without resting |

### Effort level
Some sessions in the plans in this section use an effort level from 1 to 10 to tell you how hard you should be pushing yourself. Here's what the numbers mean.

**1-4** Easy up to a gentle pace
**5-6** Able to have a conversation
**6-7** Getting out of breath
**8-9** Can't talk, uncomfortable
**10** Flat-out sprint

| ■ Week 7 | ■ Week 8 | ■ Week 9 | ■ Week 10 | ■ Week 11 | ■ Week 12 |
|---|---|---|---|---|---|
| **Monday**<br>Rest | **Monday**<br>Rest | **Monday**<br>Rest | **Monday**<br>Rest | **Monday**<br>Rest | **Monday**<br>Rest |
| **Tuesday**<br>Interval session: bike 4x10 mins at level 8, with 2 mins recovery at level 4 between reps | **Tuesday**<br>Interval session: bike 5x10 mins at level 8, with 2 mins recovery at level 4 between reps | **Tuesday**<br>Brick session: bike 8km, run 4km without resting | **Tuesday**<br>Brick session: bike 8km, run 4km without resting | **Tuesday**<br>Brick interval session: swim 400m, run 4x400m at level 9, with 2 mins recovery at level 4 between reps | **Tuesday**<br>Swim 400m |
| **Wednesday**<br>Swim 10x50m at level 8, with 2 mins recovery at level 4 between reps | **Wednesday**<br>Swim 12x50m at level 8, with 2 mins recovery at level 4 between reps | **Wednesday**<br>Swim 800m | **Wednesday**<br>Swim 800m | **Wednesday**<br>Interval session: swim 6x100m at level 8, with 2 mins recovery at level 4 between reps | **Wednesday**<br>Bike 8km |
| **Thursday**<br>Run 3x10 mins at level 8, with 2 mins recovery at level 4 between reps | **Thursday**<br>Run 4x10 mins at level 8, with 2 mins recovery at level 4 between reps | **Thursday**<br>Bike 10km | **Thursday**<br>Bike 20km | **Thursday**<br>Rest | **Thursday**<br>Run 3km |
| **Friday**<br>Rest | **Friday**<br>Rest | **Friday**<br>Run 5km | **Friday**<br>Run 5km | **Friday**<br>Bike 15km | **Friday**<br>Rest |
| **Saturday**<br>Swim 800m | **Saturday**<br>Swim 800m | **Saturday**<br>Bike 20km | **Saturday**<br>Interval session: swim 10x50m at level 8, with 2 mins recovery at level 4 between reps | **Saturday**<br>Rest | **Saturday**<br>Rest |
| **Sunday**<br>Brick session: bike 8km, run 4km without resting | **Sunday**<br>Brick session: bike 8km, run 4km without resting | **Sunday**<br>Run 6km | **Sunday**<br>Bike 10km | **Sunday**<br>Interval session: bike 10x1km at level 8-9, with 2 mins recovery at level 4 between reps | **Sunday**<br>Sprint triathlon |

# Olympic plan weeks 1-18

## This six-month plan will help you conquer the classic distance

The Olympic version of triathlon (1,500m swim, 40km bike, 10km run) has developed into the sport's classic distance and is a significant test of cardiovascular endurance. This plan assumes a base level of fitness and, ideally, you should have completed a shorter triathlon before you attempt your first Olympic-distance race. It includes approximately one brick session a week to get you familiar with doing more than one discipline in the same session. The second half of the plan focuses on building endurance by going further than the race distances in individual sessions for each of the three disciplines. After that you should do some higher-intensity sessions to hone your speed, before tapering off in the last couple of weeks to make sure you're fresh for race day.

| ■ Week 1 | ■ Week 2 | ■ Week 3 | ■ Week 4 | ■ Week 5 | ■ Week 6 |
|---|---|---|---|---|---|
| **Monday**<br>Rest | **Monday**<br>Rest | **Monday**<br>Rest | **Monday**<br>Rest | **Monday**<br>Rest | **Monday**<br>Rest |
| **Tuesday**<br>Swim 300m | **Tuesday**<br>Swim 300m | **Tuesday**<br>Swim 500m | **Tuesday**<br>Swim 500m | **Tuesday**<br>Swim 500m | **Tuesday**<br>Swim 500m |
| **Wednesday**<br>Bike 10km | **Wednesday**<br>Bike 16km | **Wednesday**<br>Bike 16km | **Wednesday**<br>Bike 16km | **Wednesday**<br>Bike 20km | **Wednesday**<br>Bike 20km |
| **Thursday**<br>Run 4km | **Thursday**<br>Run 5km | **Thursday**<br>Run 6km | **Thursday**<br>Run 6km | **Thursday**<br>Run 8km | **Thursday**<br>Run 8km |
| **Friday**<br>Rest | **Friday**<br>Rest | **Friday**<br>Rest | **Friday**<br>Rest | **Friday**<br>Rest | **Friday**<br>Rest |
| **Saturday**<br>Swim 300m | **Saturday**<br>Brick session: swim 300m, bike 10km without resting | **Saturday**<br>Brick session: swim 300m, run 5km without resting | **Saturday**<br>Brick session: bike 12km, run 5km without resting | **Saturday**<br>Brick session: swim 500m, bike 16km without resting | **Saturday**<br>Brick session: swim 500m, run 5km without resting |
| **Sunday**<br>Bike 16km | **Sunday**<br>Run 5km | **Sunday**<br>Run 5km | **Sunday**<br>Swim 300m | **Sunday**<br>Run 5km | **Sunday**<br>Bike 16km |

**Effort level**

Some sessions in the plans in this section use an effort level from 1 to 10 to tell you how hard you should be pushing yourself. Here's what the numbers mean.

**1-4** Easy up to a gentle pace
**5-6** Able to have a conversation
**6-7** Getting out of breath
**8-9** Can't talk, uncomfortable
**10** Flat-out sprint

## ■ Week 7

**Monday**
Rest

**Tuesday**
Swim 750m

**Wednesday**
Bike 16km

**Thursday**
Run 5km

**Friday**
Rest

**Saturday**
Brick session: bike 16km, run 5km without resting

**Sunday**
Swim 500m

## ■ Week 8

**Monday**
Rest

**Tuesday**
Swim 750m

**Wednesday**
Bike 16km

**Thursday**
Run 5km

**Friday**
Rest

**Saturday**
Brick session: swim 300m, bike 10km without resting

**Sunday**
Run 5km

## ■ Week 9

**Monday**
Rest

**Tuesday**
Swim 1,000m

**Wednesday**
Bike 25km

**Thursday**
Run 8km

**Friday**
Rest

**Saturday**
Brick session: bike 15km, run 5km without resting

**Sunday**
Bike 16km

## ■ Week 10

**Monday**
Rest

**Tuesday**
Swim 1,000m

**Wednesday**
Bike 25km

**Thursday**
Run 8km

**Friday**
Rest

**Saturday**
Brick session: bike 16km, run 5km without resting

**Sunday**
Swim 500m

## ■ Week 11

**Monday**
Rest

**Tuesday**
Swim 1,250m

**Wednesday**
Bike 25km

**Thursday**
Run 8km

**Friday**
Rest

**Saturday**
Brick session: swim 750m, bike 25km without resting

**Sunday**
Run 5km

## ■ Week 12

**Monday**
Rest

**Tuesday**
Swim 1,250m

**Wednesday**
Bike 25km

**Thursday**
Run 8km

**Friday**
Rest

**Saturday**
Brick session: bike 15km, run 5km without resting

**Sunday**
Bike 25km

## ■ Week 13

**Monday**
Rest

**Tuesday**
Swim 1,500m

**Wednesday**
Bike 30km

**Thursday**
Run 8km

**Friday**
Rest

**Saturday**
Brick session: bike 25km, run 5km without resting

**Sunday**
Swim 750m

## ■ Week 14

**Monday**
Rest

**Tuesday**
Swim 1,500m

**Wednesday**
Bike 30km

**Thursday**
Run 8km

**Friday**
Rest

**Saturday**
Brick session: swim 1,000m, bike 25km without resting

**Sunday**
Run 5km

## ■ Week 15

**Monday**
Rest

**Tuesday**
Swim 1,750m

**Wednesday**
Bike 40km

**Thursday**
Run 10km

**Friday**
Rest

**Saturday**
Brick session: swim 1,000m, run 5km without resting

**Sunday**
Bike 25km

## ■ Week 16

**Monday**
Rest

**Tuesday**
Swim 1,750m

**Wednesday**
Bike 40km

**Thursday**
Run 10km

**Friday**
Rest

**Saturday**
Brick session: bike 25km, run 6km without resting

**Sunday**
Swim 1,000m

## ■ Week 17

**Monday**
Rest

**Tuesday**
Swim 2,000m

**Wednesday**
Bike 50km

**Thursday**
Run 12km

**Friday**
Rest

**Saturday**
Brick session: swim 1,250m, bike 25km without resting

**Sunday**
Run 6km

## ■ Week 18

**Monday**
Rest

**Tuesday**
Swim 2,000m

**Wednesday**
Bike 50km

**Thursday**
Run 12km

**Friday**
Rest

**Saturday**
Brick session: bike 25km, run 6km without resting

**Sunday**
Bike 30km

# Olympic plan weeks 19-24

| ■ Week 19 | ■ Week 20 | ■ Week 21 | ■ Week 22 | ■ Week 23 | ■ Week 24 |
|---|---|---|---|---|---|
| **Monday**<br>Rest | **Monday**<br>Rest | **Monday**<br>Rest | **Monday**<br>Rest | **Monday**<br>Rest | **Monday**<br>Rest |
| **Tuesday**<br>Swim 1,500m | **Tuesday**<br>Swim 1,500m | **Tuesday**<br>Swim 1,250m | **Tuesday**<br>Swim 1,250m | **Tuesday**<br>Swim 1,000m | **Tuesday**<br>Swim 500m |
| **Wednesday**<br>Bike 40km | **Wednesday**<br>Bike 40km | **Wednesday**<br>Bike 30km | **Wednesday**<br>Bike 30km | **Wednesday**<br>Bike 16km | **Wednesday**<br>Bike 16km |
| **Thursday**<br>Run 10km | **Thursday**<br>Run 10km | **Thursday**<br>Run 10km | **Thursday**<br>Run 8km | **Thursday**<br>Run 8km | **Thursday**<br>Run 5km |
| **Friday**<br>Rest | **Friday**<br>Rest | **Friday**<br>Rest | **Friday**<br>Rest | **Friday**<br>Rest | **Friday**<br>Rest |
| **Saturday**<br>Swim 8x100m at level 8, with 2 mins recovery at level 4 between reps | **Saturday**<br>Interval session: bike 6x10 mins at level 8, with 2 mins recovery at level 4 between reps | **Saturday**<br>Brick session: bike 30km, run 8km without resting | **Saturday**<br>Brick session: bike 30km, run 5km without resting | **Saturday**<br>Brick session: bike 16km, run 5km without resting | **Saturday**<br>Rest |
| **Sunday**<br>Interval session: bike 5x10 mins at level 8, with 2 mins recovery at level 4 between reps | **Sunday**<br>Run 4x10 mins at level 8, with 2 mins recovery at level 4 between reps | **Sunday**<br>Bike 40km | **Sunday**<br>Swim 1,000m | **Sunday**<br>Swim 750m | **Sunday**<br>Olympic triathlon |

## Effort level

Some sessions in the plans in this section use an effort level from 1 to 10 to tell you how hard you should be pushing yourself. Here's what the numbers mean.

**1-4** Easy up to a gentle pace
**5-6** Able to have a conversation
**6-7** Getting out of breath
**8-9** Can't talk, uncomfortable
**10** Flat-out sprint

# Top 10 UK triathlons

## Put your training to the test in Britain's best triathlons

### Eton Super Sprints, May

This early season race gives you a chance to see whether your pre-season training has been up to scratch. The 400m swim is in Dorney Lake, the 20km four-lap bike course is flat, but can force riders into a head wind in the back straight. The 5km run is also hill free, so you can go for a fast finish.
**humanrace.co.uk/eton**

### Blenheim Triathlon, June

This is one of Britain's most picturesque triathlons, set in the grounds of Blenheim Palace. It's also the UK's second biggest, with over 5,000 places across the sprint, super-sprint and relay categories. The swim is staged in Blenheim Lake, the cycle and run courses take you through the palace grounds and the transitions take place in the courtyard.
**theblenheimtriathlon.com**

### Windsor Triathlon, June

Another race in a palatial setting. This time you run past Windsor Castle after swimming in the Thames and riding through a course that finishes in Windsor Great Park. The stunning venue, high-quality field and the chance for amateurs to race on the same bill as elites has on several occasions earned this event the title of British Triathlon Association Race Of The Year.
**humanrace.co.uk/windsor**

### Salford Triathlon, July

An ITU World Cup event that gives amateurs a chance to race against 200 elites. It's the only World-Cup-status

Eton Super Sprints

race staged in the UK and involves a 1,500m swim across the Salford Quays, a 40km bike course that goes past Manchester United's Old Trafford football stadium and a 10km run.
**visitsalford.info/triathlon**

### CowMan, July

This half-Ironman-distance race is for experienced triahltetes. The 1.9km swim is in open water, the 92km bike stage is two long laps and the 21km run involves some off-road sections, but is relatively flat.
**big-cow.com**

### London Triathlon, August

The world's biggest triathlon attracts over 13,000 competitors. Olympic, sprint and super-sprint distances are on offer and the course takes racers along the Thames, before weaving through the gleaming towers of Docklands.
**thelondontriathlon.com**

### Ironman UK, August

The UK's only official Ironman-distance race involves a 3.8km swim, a 180km bike ride and a 42km run. Completing the course is an achievement in itself but, if you really feel like pushing it, top finishers earn themselves a place in the Ironman World Championship in Hawaii later in the year.
**ironmanuk.com**

### Newquay Classic Triathlon, September

This exciting but testing race starts with a challenging sea swim off picturesque Lusty Glaze Beach. Once you're out of the water, you start a 40km bike ride on an undulating route to Padstow, before finishing with a 10km run along a coastal path.
**votwo.co.uk**

### Brighton Triathlon, September

A new event offering Olympic, sprint and super-sprint distances. It starts with a sea swim, before sending you off on a bike ride round a flat closed course. It finishes with a run along the seafront. Stops for ice cream and candy floss are optional.
**urbanrace.co.uk**

### Vitruvian Triathlon, September

At roughly half-Ironman distance, this is a serious test of fitness. The 1.9km swim is in Rutland Water and the 85km bike leg, which features nearly 1,000m of ascents, involves completing two circuits. The four-lap 21km run is only marginally less brutal.
**pacesetterevents.com**

The Olympic distance
Windsor Triathlon takes
racers past the castle

BIKE
OUT